GREAT GRAPHING

Activities for Collecting, Displaying, and Using Data in Grades 1–4

By Martin Lee and Marcia Miller

SCHOLASTIC
PROFESSIONAL BOOKS

New York • Toronto • London • Auckland • Sydney

To Fred, Stu-Guy, Nancy, Sam, Mr. Sam, Mary
Anne, Glenn, Julie, Bo, Susan, Tom, Trudy,
Kathy, Ben, Mimi, and all the other
great teachers we've worked with.

Cover design by Vincent Ceci
Cover photograph by Anthony Loew
Interior design and illustrations by Drew Hires
ISBN 0-590-49470-8
Copyright ©1993 by Martin Lee and Marcia Miller. All rights reserved.
12 11 10 9 8 7 6 5 4 3   4 5 / 9
Printed in the U.S.A.

TABLE OF CONTENTS

INTRODUCTION

Children are natural data seekers and gatherers. They're curious about *how* and *why* and *where* and *who* and *how many* and *how much*. They ask questions all the time. Have you heard any of these lately?

◆ What's your favorite animal?

◆ Who did you vote for to be president?

◆ How many of you have seen a real dinosaur skeleton?

◆ Which food do you hate the most?

◆ How long can you hold your breath?

In today's high-tech world, data bombard us at every turn—on TV, on the radio, in newspapers and magazines, on our computer screens. Some data have staggering significance, such as the number of people starving in Somalia or the number of homeless families in America. But data can also be more modest, such as the choices on channel 5 tonight, last week's top video rentals, or calorie counts in favorite foods.

How can people absorb so much data? One way is through visual organizers, such as graphs and tables. But these tools aren't just for statisticians or pollsters. Graphing provides a way for children to organize information clearly so that they can grasp its meaning more readily. Graphing belongs in every classroom.

The National Council of Teachers of Mathematics (NCTM) thinks so, too. According to Standard 11 of the NCTM *Curriculum and Evaluation Standards for School Mathematics,* children in grades K–4 should have many experiences in which they do the following:

- *collect, organize, and describe data;*
- *construct, read, and interpret displays of data;*
- *formulate and solve problems that involve collecting and analyzing data.*

In an information-rich environment, it's increasingly important for children to be able to use graphs not only to organize and display data, but also as tools for solving problems in their own world. Children don't automatically know how to sort, arrange, label, and display data, but this book can help *you* help *them* with these key skills. Children can become adept at interpreting what's presented in tables and graphs. And they need opportunities to collect, organize, and display data for themselves.

Learning about graphs and graphing can benefit children in many ways. For one thing, graphing encourages an investigative spirit as children generate questions, make conjectures, and look for relationships. Graphing involves higher-level critical thinking skills, such as making predictions, prioritizing, looking for patterns, drawing conclusions, and adjusting assumptions. For another, it reinforces children's communication skills as they discuss and write about their methods and discoveries. They can learn to use the graph that best suits their needs. They can debate how some graphs can give a different slant on the same data, or that sometimes a table may be more useful than a graph. And graphing helps children appreciate how useful math can be in the world outside the classroom.

ABOUT THIS BOOK

Scan the table of contents of *Great Graphing* and flip through the pages. You'll notice that the book is divided into three parts. You'll see a variety of activities designed for the elementary grades that use an assortment of hands-on and classroom materials.

Part 1: Graphing Activities: Collecting, Displaying, and Using Data is the longest section and most central to the focus of the book. It contains activities in which children collect data, examine it, organize it, graph it, think about it, and report on it. The pages are organized by graph type. Within that arrangement, they appear in sequence from the concrete to the abstract. For example, in the bar graph section, the initial activities have children using only real objects; next, they progress to using pictures and symbols, and finally to bars.

Activities are presented with step-by-step directions for you to follow, including a list of necessary materials, teaching tips, helpful wrap-up questions you might want to ask, and suggestions for altering or extending the activity. Some activities also contain related pages you can duplicate and distribute to your class.

Sprinkled throughout the section you'll find Data Dazzlers. These are terrific tidbits to tickle fact lovers of all ages. They may inspire you to hunt for your own class Data Dazzlers together. They may lead to discussions, measurement or comparison activities, and maybe even some graphs of dazzling proportion.

Part 2: Reproducible Student Pages: Interpreting Data is comprised of reproducible pages with graph interpretation activities that children can complete on their own. The pages are organized in order of increasing difficulty within graph type. Children answer questions based on given graphs. They summarize information a graph shows or describe what a graph *doesn't* show. They use logic or critical thinking skills to make or complete graphs. In some activities, children must decide which of two graphs more effectively presents certain data, or which graph matches data displayed in another form.

Part 3: Reproducible Teacher Resources contains forms that will come in handy for these and other graphing activities you'll undertake with your class. Look here for grid paper, blank tally tables, a pictograph form, and other helpful pages. Feel free to customize these generic forms to suit a particular activity, or substitute a similar form you may already have on hand. The symbol ▼ shows that an activity calls for a Teacher Resource.

TEACHING TIPS

✔ Go through the book as you see fit, doing the activities in any order that makes sense for your class or schedule.

✔ You may find that some activities are too advanced for your class, while others may be too basic. Some may take more time than you have. Feel free to revise tasks to suit your students, or extend them if results suggest further investigation.

✔ Although the activities are self-contained, think of them as resources for integrating data analysis into other areas of your curriculum. Graphing offers a natural bridge between math and social studies, ecology, or science, so look for opportunities to weave these techniques and strategies into broader projects your class undertakes.

✔ Help children recognize that data come in many forms and that there may be several ways to display the same data. Encourage children to try using different graphs to show the same information and see what conclusions they draw.

✔ Try to make children feel comfortable about graphs so that they'll begin to spot natural opportunities to use graphs. A good place to start might be with graphing their after-school activities.

✔ Encourage talking, questioning, sharing, recording, and summarizing during these activities.

✔ Set up a graph corner in your classroom—part of a bulletin board, a special loose-leaf notebook, an accordion folder—so you and your children can collect examples of graphs from magazines and newspapers. *USA Today* is an especially good source of colorful, easy-to-read graphs on many topics.

✔ To make class activites run more smoothly, gather some useful materials such as the following:

◆ a floor mat with grid lines (put colored tape on a drop cloth or sew felt strips onto a sheet);
◆ grid paper in many sizes;
◆ paper squares for bulletin board graphs;
◆ rubber stamps or stickers for pictographs;
◆ snap cubes or other small objects for tallying.

Now, take a deep breath and dive in for some great graphing!

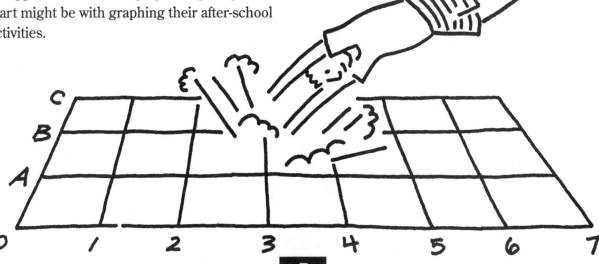

Part 1

Graphing Activities: Collecting, Displaying and Using Data

INTRODUCTION TO TALLIES AND TABLES

Most children enjoy counting objects or events, but it isn't always obvious to them how to keep track of what they count. That's where tallying can be a great help. Tallies are an easy tool for keeping count of data as it happens, especially for data that are sorted as they are counted. The typical method of making tallies is to group by fives. Children will learn to make four vertical marks (strokes) crossed diagonally by a fifth mark that forms each "bundle" for easy counting later.

Tables appear so commonly that children may already be familiar with some of them—calendars, class schedules, attendance charts, seating plans, TV timetables, and lunch menus, to name a few. The tally and table activities in this section move from the concrete to the more abstract. They are organized to help children see how to keep track as they count, to total and compare results, to organize data into various tabular forms, and to explore ways to adjust tables to highlight particular aspects of the same data.

Look for reproducible tallies and table activities in Part 2 on pages 69 and 70.

RELATED SKILLS
- one-to-one correspondence
- counting and comparing
- skip-counting by 5s; counting from a given multiple of 5
- distinguishing between horizontal and vertical

EVERY TABLE HAS
- a title
- rows and columns
- descriptive labels for rows and columns
- tallies or numbers to represent data

FAST FACTS ABOUT TALLIES AND TABLES
- Tallies are useful for collecting data; after data have been gathered, tallies may be counted and the numerals written in a table.
- Tables can have as many rows or columns as necessary to suit the data.
- Some tables give cumulative totals for related data.

FIVE STEPS TO A TABLE
1. Make as many rows and columns as you need.
2. Label the rows and columns.
3. Fill in data in the appropriate spaces in the form of tallies or numbers.
4. Find totals or subtotals as necessary.
5. Write a title above the table.

Use the tables on the next page as teaching tools. Copy them onto the chalkboard, or chart paper, or make transparencies of them to use with an overhead projector.

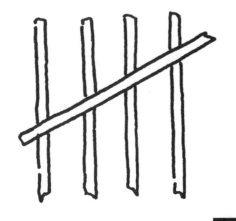
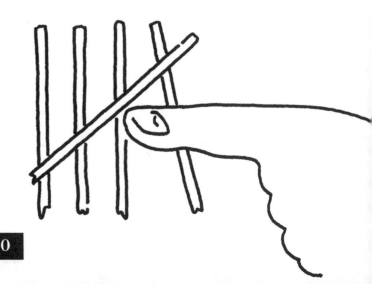

10

SNEEZES ON TUESDAY

TITLE

LABELS FOR COLUMNS

Person	Tallies
Meg	卌 I
Tim	III
Fred	IIII
Ann-Marie	卌 IIII
Jewel	卌 II

DATA SHOWN WITH TALLY MARKS

SNEEZES ON TUESDAY

TITLE

LABELS FOR COLUMNS

Person	No. of Sneezes
Meg	6
Tim	3
Fred	4
Ann-Marie	9
Jewel	7

DATA SHOWN USING NUMBERS

TALLY TIME!
Children bundle toothpicks to learn about tallying.

Materials
toothpicks • modeling clay

Here's What To Do

1. Distribute toothpicks and a small lump of clay to each child. Tell the children that you will clap some rhythms. Their job is to listen carefully and stick one toothpick into the clay for each clap they hear. Then start clapping (3 to 8 claps or so). After each round of claps, have children count the toothpicks they used to see whether their tallies agree.

2. Collect the clay and repeat the activity. This time, challenge children to find their own ways to keep count using toothpicks—but don't guide them. Talk about the methods they used for tallying.

3. Now read a list of 20 to 25 words the children can tally. (You can use the list given.) After the children have made their toothpick tallies, ask them how to make the toothpicks easier to count. Some may say to group them by 2s, 5s, or 10s. Highlight grouping by 5s as the plan mathematicians use. Demonstrate how to lay out 4 toothpicks and place the fifth one across to signal a bundle of 5. Have children practice this. Then repeat some of the tallying activities and have children bundle toothpicks by 5s.

Wrap It Up
- What does it mean to make a tally? How is tallying like counting? How is it different?
- Have you ever seen grownups tally things? Where? When? How?
- How can you keep track in a similar way but without using toothpicks?

And Then...
- Small groups can take turns clapping, snapping, winking, or performing other simple, recurring actions for others to tally with toothpicks.
- Try another toothpick tally tomorrow to determine how many times people sharpen their pencils. Put some toothpicks by the class pencil sharpener, so children can tally as they sharpen.

WORD LIST

tooth	tiger	tulip
tree	tennis	ticklish
trumpet	tub	trouble
twinkle	truck	tomato
television	taxi	taco
turtle	telephone	tongue
toy	tabby	type
tuna		tunnel
toad		trash

Tip
- Some children bundle the toothpicks after they already have 5, so the bundle actually has 6 toothpicks. Help them get used to using the cross bar as the fifth tally.

DATA DAZZLER
An average box of flat toothpicks has 750 toothpicks. If you laid them end to end, you could form a toothpick train longer than 3 school buses!

RHYME-TIME TALLY

Tally key rhyming words in a poem or song.

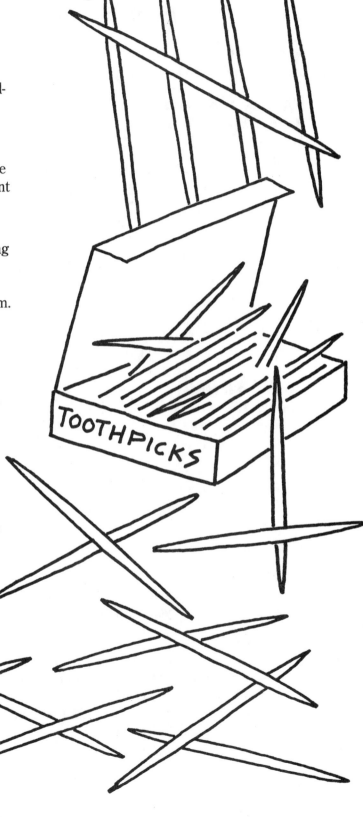

Here's What To Do

1. Pick a poem or song in which words are repeated. Decide on a key word to listen for.

2. Recite the poem or sing the song. Challenge children to tally each time they hear the key word spoken or sung. They can use toothpicks or paper-and-pencil tallies.

3. Repeat the activity with a different word from the same song or poem. Then try again with different songs or poems.

And Then...

◆ Ask children which they think is harder—tallying something they see or something they hear.

◆ Have children guess which word they think is used most often in another familiar song or poem. Different children can tally different words. Compare tallies to determine the outcome.

At Home

◆ Have children ask their parents when they've used tally marks. Children can report their findings to the class.

◆ The family can pick a TV commercial to watch together and tally how many times a product name is said.

◆ According to the *Guinness Book of Records,* "Happy Birthday to You" is sung more than any other English-language song in the world. Have children tally how many times family members can sing it in one minute.

JUST A MINUTE HERE!

In two quick tally activities, children record the number of blinks and the number of times they can spell their names aloud in 1 minute.

Materials
paper and pencil • clock with second hand (or stopwatch or timer) • toothpicks

BLINK 'N' THINK
Here's What To Do

1. Group children in 3s—one child times, one child tallies, and one child blinks.

2. The timer keeps track for 1 minute as the blinker looks around the room, blinking normally. The tally keeper makes a tally every time the blinker blinks. Each child can decide whether to use toothpicks or paper-and-pencil tallies.

3. Be sure everyone gets to blink, tally, and time. Then discuss what happened.
◆ Did everyone blink the same number of times in a minute? What *did* happen?
◆ How did you tally the blinks?

SPELLBOUND
Here's What To Do

1. Time for trios again. This time you need a timer, a tally keeper, and a speller.

2. The timer keeps track for 1 minute. The speller spells his or her first name aloud as many times as possible in a minute. The tally keeper makes a tally for each complete spelling. It's important for the tally keeper to write the speller's name as well as the tallies so that children will know why Ed's results were different from Mary Elizabeth's.

3. As before, children take turns at each role.

Wrap It Up
◆ What were your results? How can you explain all the differences in our class?
◆ What would make your own results change?

And Then...
Here are some other activities children count on:
◆ How many times can you spell your *last* name in a minute?
◆ How many times can you *write* your name in a minute?
◆ How many times can you count to 20 in a minute?

Tip
◆ Instead of having children time the blinks with a clock or stopwatch, play or sing a familiar song. Its duration becomes the amount of time for keeping track.

DATA DAZZLER
A girl in Texas has a first name with 1,019 letters. For this activity, she'd be better off using her middle name—it only has 36 letters!

SHAKE, RATTLE, AND TALLY

Children tally 2 elements at a time while practicing number facts for 5.

Materials
two-color counters • small paper cups • Teacher Resource Sheet ▼**1**

Here's What To Do
1. If necessary, make two-color counters by placing a sticker or a piece of masking tape on one side of a checker or a plastic chip. Or paint on spots with polish.

2. Give each child 5 two-color counters in a paper cup. Talk about the different combinations of red and yellow sides that can show when you spill out the counters. (If your counters have other colors, that's fine, too.)

3. Have the children shake the cup, spill out the 5 counters, and tally how many of each color comes up. Children can use ▼**1** as a tally table. Help them label the rows and columns to fit the task.

4. Have kids shake, rattle, and tally their counters 10 times.

Wrap It Up
◆ Which color came up more often? How does your tally table show this?
◆ How many tallies have you made in all? How many *should* there be?
◆ What do you think would happen if you shake, rattle, and tally 10 more times? Go ahead and see!

And Then...
◆ Take things a step further. Combine individual tallies into a class tally that examines how many times each color came up for the class as a whole.
◆ To shake things up a bit more, try a similar investigation with 10 two-color counters.

Tip
◆ From here on, the activities require children to tally 2 or more elements.

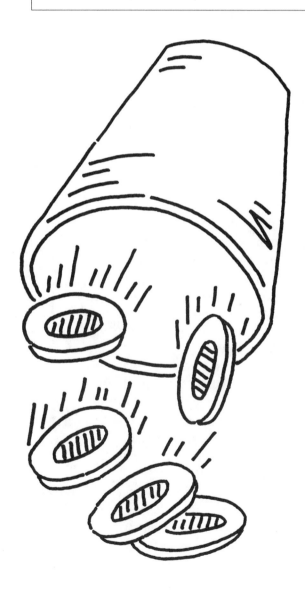

TIC-TAC-TALLY

Tally wins, losses, and ties in a familiar game.

Congratulations! Your class has been invited to participate in the Intergalactic Tic-Tac-Toe Tournament to be held on the Moon next July. How can you decide who'll go? One way is to hold a Tic-Tac-Toe tournament and tally the results.

Materials
Teacher Resource Sheet

Here's What To Do

1. Be sure everyone knows how to play Tic-Tac-Toe.

2. Talk about all the possible outcomes in a game of Tic-Tac-Toe and how best to tally them. It will work best if each player has a tally table with the categories WIN, LOSE, and TIE. Children can make this table using ▼.

3. Help children pair off to play 5 games of Tic-Tac-Toe. Remind them to tally the outcome of each game in their table. After 5 games, children change partners to play 5 more games, again tallying every outcome. Repeat until each child has played 20 games.

Wrap It Up

◆ How did most games end—as wins, losses, or ties? Combine individual results into one large class tally table to find out.

◆ How many games of Tic-Tac-Toe did the class play? How can you figure it out? (HINT: Be careful! For every win, there's a loss! And it takes two to tie.)

◆ Is there a class champion for the Intergalactic Tic-Tac-Toe Tournament? Is there more than one? What about the whole class? How could you decide?

Tips

◆ At the end of a game, 2 tallies are made—one for each player. If one person won, another person lost. If the game was a tie, both players mark that tie.

◆ Children can check that they have played 20 games by counting all the WIN, LOSE, and TIE tallies.

ADOPT-A-CRITTER

A class survey shows which zoo animals children would most like to adopt.

Materials

Teacher Resource sheet

Here's What To Do

1. Brainstorm a list of zoo animals the children imagine adopting. List all their ideas. Then discuss the list, eliminating any animals that the group agrees are too dangerous, would be too frightened, or might present special problems. Eventually, pare the list down to about 6 animals.

2. Ask each child to vote on the zoo animal he or she would most like to adopt. Record one vote at a time by making tallies in the correct place on the table. When everyone has voted, total the tallies. List the animals in order of preference.

3. Have the children make their own copy of the list of adoptable animals using . Over the next few days, they should explain the zoo adoption idea to other people to find out their choices, tallying the votes just as you did. Encourage children to bring their tally tables to lunch and to recess. They can survey family members, friends, and neighbors after school.

Wrap It Up

◆ What did you find out about people's preferences for adopting zoo animals?

◆ Did your own survey show the same results as the class survey?

◆ Did the results surprise you? How would you explain the differences (or similarities)?

◆ Do you have any ideas about why people voted as they did?

And Then...

Have children survey classmates on another topic and tally the results. Try one of these:

◆ favorite ice cream flavor

◆ least favorite cereal

◆ most beloved toy

◆ the best way to spend a Saturday

◆ funniest TV show

MELTS IN YOUR MOUTH

Predict, count, sort, tally, and analyze M & M's.

Materials
M&M's (one bag per pair of children) • paper plates or napkins • Teacher Resource Sheet

Here's What To Do
1. Talk about what the children expect to find in a bag of M&M's—how many pieces, what colors, how many of each color, and so on.

2. Have children pair up. Hand out the M&M's.

3. Children pour the candy onto a paper plate or napkin. Using , they list the different colors and tally the number of pieces of each color.

Wrap It Up
◆ Do all bags contain the same colors? The same number of candies?
◆ Which colors show up most often? Least often?
◆ Who's got the bag *you* want? Why?
◆ What would happen if the whole class combined the results into one large tally? Try it! What conclusions can you draw?

And Then...
Let children digest their data!

ON CALL

Phone numbers form the basis for tallies.

Here's What To Do
1. List several ways to describe a phone number, such as the following:
   • it has no zeros;
   • it has only even numbers (or only odd numbers);
   • it has repeated digits;
   • it adds up to 30 or more (or to less than 30);
   • it includes a 3- or 4-digit palindrome (reads the same backward or forward).
   List other possibilities that the children suggest.

2. Tally how many class phone numbers fit each description.

3. Challenge the class to think of other descriptions that might include a lot of phone numbers. Suggest "phone numbers that end in an odd number" as an example to get children started. Tally the results of these descriptions, too.

STICK TO THE DATES

Tallying helps determine how many number stickers are needed to make a class calendar.

Materials
calendars • Teacher Resource Sheet

Here's What To Do

1. Ask the children for their help in figuring out exactly how many of each number sticker to buy in order to make a big class calendar for the new month. Be sure they understand that to make a 2-digit number, say 14, they'd need a 1 sticker and a 4 sticker.

2. First have children guess how many digits they'll need and which digits will appear most often. Then discuss ways to find out for sure. A digit-by-digit tally will work well.

3. Have children work in pairs. Distribute calendars they can use as a reference.

4. Have children use ❷ to list the digits 0–9. They refer to their calendars to tally the digits as they appear. Children may cross off each date once its digits have been tallied.

Wrap It Up

◆ How many stickers for each digit should you buy?

◆ How many stickers will you buy in all? Any surprises?

◆ What would change if you did this tally for a different month?

And Then...

Have children use the same strategy to figure out how many digit stickers they'd need to number the pages in a book or magazine they're reading or in today's newspaper.

BOOK LOOK
Sort and tally different kinds of book pages.

Materials
Teachers Resource Sheet

Here's What To Do
1. Talk about the usual ways to examine a book: read the title, flip through the pages, look at the book jacket, and so on. Then ask children which kinds of pages they think they'd find most often in a book: pages with only words, pages with only pictures, or pages with words and pictures.

2. Help children form pairs to examine a book. They will need a tally table like this one, which they can make using ▼**1** .

PAGES WITH	TALLIES	TOTAL
Words *only*		
Pictures *only*		
Words *and* Pictures		

3. Have partners pick a book of 50 pages or less. They can flip through the book quickly to guess which kind of page they'll find most often. Then they should begin their investigation, tallying each page according to one of the categories they have on their tally table. When children have completed their tallies, they should total the tally marks in the TOTAL column.

Wrap It Up
◆ Did you find what you expected to find?
◆ Did you need any other category, such as *Blank Pages* or *Pages with Numbers*?
◆ Who might need to know information like this?
◆ Do you think the results would be different for a math book? For a comic book? For a board book for toddlers? Why?

At Home
Children can do a similar analysis of a magazine or newspaper with family members or caretakers. Have them look at each page and tally it in the same way. Talk about other categories they might need, such as *Pages with Ads, Photographs,* or *Graphs.*

In class the next day, have children compare their findings. They can post their tables on the bulletin board, make presentations to the class, or have small-group discussions. Which newspapers have the most stories? The most photos? The most pictures?

LIGHTS OUT

Take a week-long tally of class bedtimes.

Here's What To Do

1. Post a large tally chart that lists a range of bedtimes, like this one:

before 7:00	7:00	7:30	8:00	8:30	9:00	9:30	10:00	10:30	11:00	11:30	12:00	after 12:00

2. Ask children what time they went to bed last night. As each child responds, make a tally in the appropriate part of the chart. Figure out with the class how to record bedtimes such as 8:15 or 7:55. Then tell the children that when they come in tomorrow morning, they should make a tally for the time they go to bed tonight.

3. Repeat this activity every morning for a week. Each child will make 5 tallies in all, but where the tally appears may change from day to day.

Wrap It Up
◆ What does the tally table show about class bedtimes?
◆ Which is the latest bedtime? The earliest?
◆ Which is the most common bedtime?
◆ How might the data change if we included Friday and Saturday nights?

And Then...
◆ Try a similar wake-up tally.
◆ Have children tally parent or sibling bedtimes for a week.

DATA DAZZLER

When Robert McDonald went to bed on April 2, 1986, he probably fell asleep fast. McDonald had been awake for the previous 452 hours and 40 minutes!

NOODLING AROUND

Tally alphabet noodles to find out which letter appears most often in alphabet soup.

Materials
uncooked alphabet noodles • paper cups • Alphabet Noodle Tally Table (page 23)

Here's What To Do
1. Ask children which letter they think appears most often in English. Ask them to name other common letters, as well as ones that appear less often. Talk about whether the frequency of occurrence would apply to the noodles in a bowl of alphabet soup.

2. Arrange children in pairs. Give each pair one-quarter cup of uncooked alphabet noodles. Hand out copies of the alphabet noodle tally sheet on the next page.

3. Have each pair tally the letters they find in their portion of noodles.

4. While pairs are tallying, make a much larger version of the tally sheet, or draw one on the chalkboard. Use it for a combined class tally.

5. As pairs finish their individual noodle tallies, invite them to transfer their results to the class tally.

Wrap It Up
- With help from the class, total the results for each letter.
- Which letters showed up most often? Are they vowels? Consonants? Both?
- Which letters appear hardly at all? Are any left out altogether?
- How do the number of **r**s compare with the number of **k**s? Try other comparisons.
- Which letters appeared about the same number of times?
- How many more times did the leading vowel appear than the leading consonant?
- Which letter showed up about twice as many times as **p** did?

And Then...
Challenge children to see how many words they can form starting with a particular letter, using only the letters in their cup. They can tally the results.

Name _____

ALPHABET NOODLE TALLY TABLE

A	
B	
C	
D	
E	
F	
G	
H	
I	
J	
K	
L	
M	
N	
O	
P	
Q	
R	
S	
T	
U	
V	
W	
X	
Y	
Z	

INTRODUCTION TO BAR GRAPHS

Because bar graphs are so commonly used, it's easy to assume that children know more about bar graphs than they actually do. Some children may grasp the basics of reading a bar graph but have had little experience constructing one.

The bar graphing activities that follow progress from the concrete to the abstract. They are organized to help children understand what a bar graph is, how to read a bar graph, how to design and construct one, and how to use a bar graph to display and interpret data. The first few activities feature graphs based on real objects. Then children work with "transitional" graphs that combine objects with visual representations of data. Finally, children use symbolic or "standard" graphs in which bars show *how many* or *how much*. They examine greater quantities or more complex relationships.

Look for reproducible bar graph activities in Part 2 on pages 71 through 76.

RELATED SKILLS
◆ sorting and classifying
◆ understanding and using tally marks
◆ counting, comparing, and recognizing numbers
◆ making, using, and interpreting tables

EVERY BAR GRAPH HAS
◆ a title
◆ two sides (the vertical and horizontal axes)
◆ descriptive labels for each side (or axis)
◆ a scale calibrated to suit the data (by 1s, 2s, 5s, 10s, 25s, etc.)

FAST FACTS ABOUT BAR GRAPHS
◆ Bars can be vertical or horizontal.
◆ The tallest (or longest) bar represents the greatest amount; the shortest bar corresponds to the least amount; bars that represent identical quantities are the same length.
◆ Bars may touch or be separated.
◆ Double bar graphs compare two related sets of data on one graph.

FIVE STEPS TO A BAR GRAPH
1. Decide whether to make the bars vertical or horizontal.
2. Draw and label the sides (axes).
3. Choose a scale; calibrate it to fit the data.
4. Draw the bars to represent your data.
5. Write a title above the graph.

Use the bar graph on the next page as a teaching tool. Copy it onto the chalkboard, or chart paper, or make a transparency of it to use with an overhead projector.

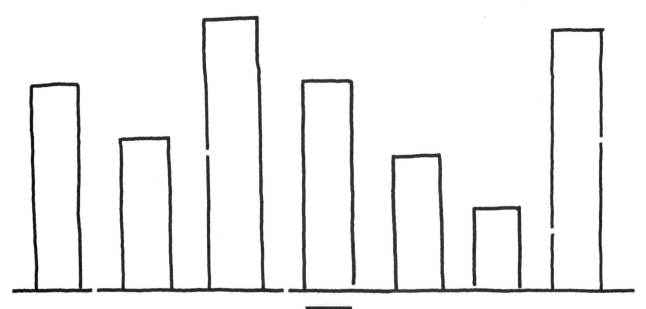

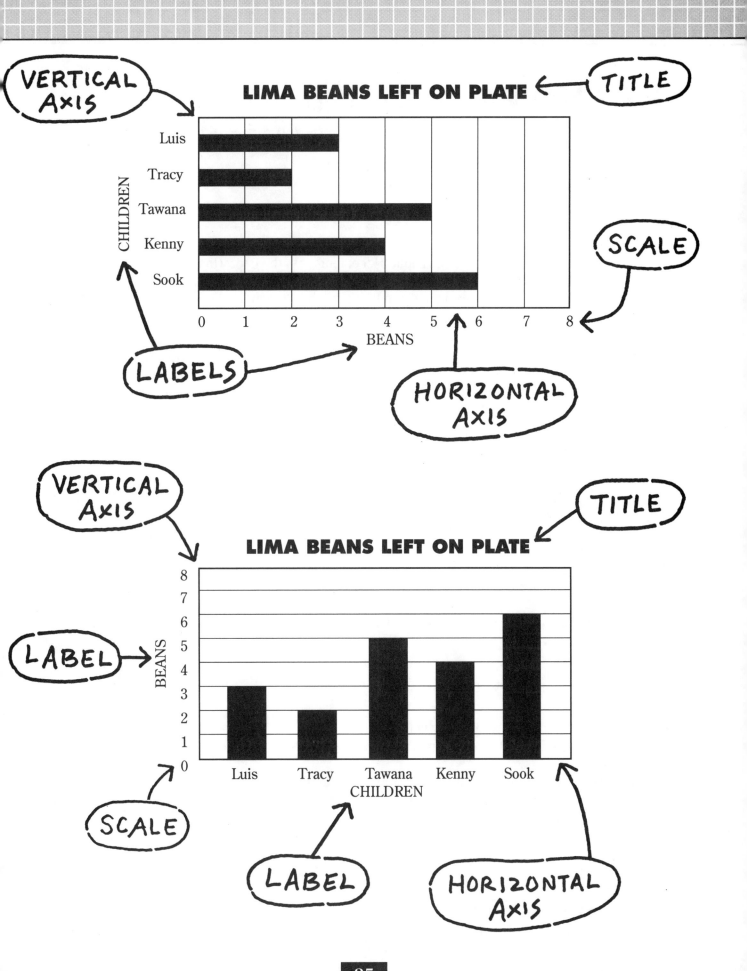

VERTICAL AXIS

TITLE

LIMA BEANS LEFT ON PLATE

CHILDREN

Luis

Tracy

Tawana

Kenny

Sook

0 1 2 3 4 5 6 7 8

BEANS

SCALE

LABELS

HORIZONTAL AXIS

VERTICAL AXIS

TITLE

LIMA BEANS LEFT ON PLATE

LABEL

BEANS

8
7
6
5
4
3
2
1
0

Luis Tracy Tawana Kenny Sook

CHILDREN

SCALE

LABEL

HORIZONTAL AXIS

SIT AND BE COUNTED

Children gather data about their birthdays for a bar graph, then form the graph by sitting in rows.

Materials
masking tape • construction paper • index cards

Here's What To Do

1. Clear a large floor space. Tape a line about 24 feet long onto the floor. (In good weather, try this outside; if you do, make the line with chalk.) On a piece of construction paper, label the line MONTHS OF THE YEAR. Place index-card labels for the 12 months at equal intervals along the line.

2. Sit cross-legged on the floor behind the month in which you were born. Then ask the children to take places on the floor behind the card that indicates the month in which they were born. Be sure children with the same birth month sit one behind the other in a row. You can call children up month by month or ask several children at a time to find their months until everyone is seated in rows.

3. Have the children look around at one another and describe what they see. Tell them that together they are a people graph that shows data on class birthdays.

Wrap It Up
◆ Which month has the most birthdays? How does our people graph show this?
◆ Do any months have just one birthday? How do we know?
◆ How can you find two months with the same number of birthdays in them? What would you look for?
◆ How can you recognize a month where there are *no* birthdays?
◆ How many children were born in months that start with **J**? With **M**? With a vowel?

And Then...
Try other people graphs. Gather birthday data for questions like these:

◆ In which season does your birthday fall?
◆ How many birthdays fall on odd-numbered days? On even-numbered days?
◆ Were you born in this community? In another community in our state? In a different state? In another country?
◆ How can we show this information on paper?

Tip
◆ Photograph the people graph and display it on a bulletin board with other bar graphs.

MOOOOO!

Use empty milk cartons to make a graph that shows how much milk the class drinks.

Materials
glue • butcher paper • empty milk cartons

Here's What To Do

1. Talk about ways to keep track of how much milk the class drinks at lunch during one week. Discuss whether that amount might change from day to day and why. Then plan a milk-carton graph to find out.

2. Each day, ask the children to save their empty milk cartons and bring them back to the classroom. Rinse them out and let them dry.

3. Glue the milk cartons together to form a long "train." Place the train on a large sheet of butcher paper that you have labeled with the days of the week. Be sure to add labels, such as DAYS OF THE WEEK and NUMBER OF CARTONS.

4. Do this for 5 days to create a graph with milk-carton "bars."

Wrap It Up

◆ What does the graph show? What title could we give it?

◆ On which day did we drink the most cartons of milk? The fewest?

◆ On which days did we drink the same number of cartons of milk?

◆ How many cartons of milk did we drink on Tuesday? On Thursday?

◆ How can we figure out how many cartons of milk we drank for the whole week?

◆ Can we make the milk-carton graph even easier to understand? How?

◆ How can we record the same data on paper?

DATA DAZZLER

Would the milk cartons on your graph fill a milk crate? In London, England on July 30, 1988, Frank Charles balanced 24 milk crates on his chin for 19 seconds!

DON'T EAT THAT GRAPH!

Multicolored candies form the bars of this graph.

Materials

Life Savers or other multicolored candies • poster paper • glue

Here's What To Do

1. Open a roll of Life Savers (or a package of another kind of candy that comes in one size and assorted colors). Have children name all the different colors they see.

2. Write each color name along one axis of a bar graph. Give the graph a title and label each axis.

3. Have children glue the candies onto the graph, according to color, to form bars. You can make one graph with the class or have pairs make their own graphs.

Wrap It Up

◆ How would you explain to someone how to read this graph?

◆ What does the graph show about colors in a roll of Life Savers? Do you think we'd find the same data in *all* rolls of Life Savers? What are some ways to find out?

◆ How can we make a different kind of bar graph to show the same data? How can boxes help?

DATA DAZZLER

According to the *Guinness Book of Records*, Life Savers are the all-time top-selling candy. If you could line up all the Life Savers ever sold end to end, they would circle the Earth about 60 times!

HAIR, HAIR!

This graph uses pasta shapes to display data about class hair types.

Materials

glue • poster paper • uncooked spaghetti for straight hair, fusilli (crimped spaghetti) for wavy hair, rotelli (corkscrews) for curly or nappy hair

Here's What To Do

1. Draw grid lines on the poster paper to prepare the bar graph. Make the boxes about 2 inches square, and indicate the axes.

2. Talk about the types of hair children in your class have. Use words like *straight, wavy, curly,* or *nappy* to form categories you can use on the bar graph.

3. Write the hair types along the vertical axis of the graph and label it TYPES OF HAIR. Give the graph a title, such as OUR HAIR. Number the horizontal axis and label it NUMBER OF CHILDREN.

4. Let children decide on the hair type that best describes their own hair.

5. Show the class the different kinds of pasta that represent the different types of hair. Have each child take a piece of the appropriate pasta and glue it in an appropriate box on the graph. Continue until everyone is represented on the graph.

Wrap It Up

◆ What hair type do most children in our class have?
◆ How many children in our class have wavy hair? Straight hair? Curly hair?
◆ How does the graph show this information? How do the boxes in each row help?
◆ How can we use the same graph to show the data without using pasta?

DATA DAZZLER

A Swedish woman reported that her hair was twice as long as she was tall. She was 5 feet 3 inches tall. How long was her hair?

And Then...

Take a nature walk to collect leaves, acorns, feathers, shells, stones, etc. Make a graph in which bars are formed by these objects glued in rows of boxes on large paper.

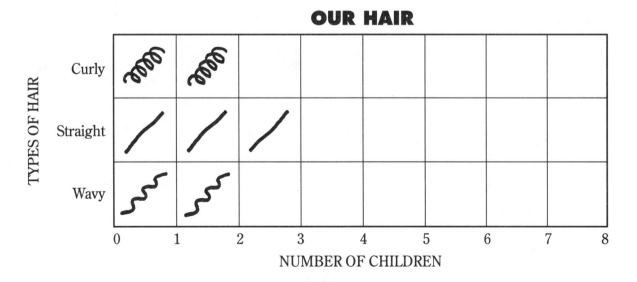

OUR HAIR

NOT ON MY PLATE!

Snap-cube bars form a hands-on graph of everyone's least favorite foods!

Materials
snap cubes • large sheet of construction paper

Here's What To Do

1. Brainstorm a list of the least favorite foods in your class. Narrow the list to 5 to 7 foods. Vote and tally, if necessary, to do this.

2. Use the construction paper to make a large bar graph. Write the name of each unpopular food along the vertical axis of the graph. Label this axis UNPOPULAR FOODS or something similar. Pick a name for the graph, maybe FOODS WE LOVE TO HATE.

3. Each child gets a snap cube to use as a vote on the graph. Children who vote for the same food snap their cubes together to form a single bar. Bars start to the right of each food name. Continue until all votes have been cast and all bars formed.

Wrap It Up

◆ What does our graph show? How does it show it?
◆ Which food is the least favorite in our class? According to the graph, which unpopular food is not as awful as the others?
◆ How can we tell if everyone voted?
◆ How will the graph change if everyone votes twice?
◆ Who might use the information this graph shows?
◆ Is there a way to record the same data on paper? How?

And Then...
With input from the children, rework the graph to show the same data in vertical form. Ask children how they could do this. Talk about which format children prefer.

At Home
Do adults and children hate the same foods? Have children survey family members to find out. Have them record the most unpopular foods among the adults they know and share the data in class the next day. Compile the results in a class bar graph that shows foods adults can't stand.

DATA DAZZLER

You may not like asparagus, but over 100,000 asparagus lovers and their friends and families attend the annual asparagus festival in Stockton, California, each April.

HOME SWEET HOME

Paper squares are the building blocks for a graph that shows dream house choices.

Materials

paper squares (about 1 1/2 in.) • thumbtacks • paper strips or crepe-paper streamers
• paper labels

Here's What To Do

1. Brainstorm a list of the most wonderful places children can imagine living in—including a castle, farm, space station, cave, tent, tree house, skyscraper, and a houseboat.

2. Vote to narrow the list to 4 to 6 places. Write the name of each place on a paper label.

3. Clear a space on a bulletin board. Attach the place labels at regular intervals along the horizontal axis of a graph. Separate the columns by paper strips. Decide on a title for the graph, such as DREAM PLACES TO LIVE. Label each axis.

4. Give each child a paper square. Demonstrate how to tack the square onto the empty graph to begin forming a bar. In turn, have children add their squares to the graph to show their preference.

Wrap It Up

◆ What does each paper square mean?
◆ What makes this a graph? What does it show? What does it *not* show?
◆ How did we form the bars? Why are some longer than others?
◆ What statements can you make from looking at our graph?
◆ How can we show this same information with pencil and paper? What kind of paper will work best?

At Home

Have children ask 5 adults the same question about dream housing. The next day, talk about how the new data compare with what the class graph shows.

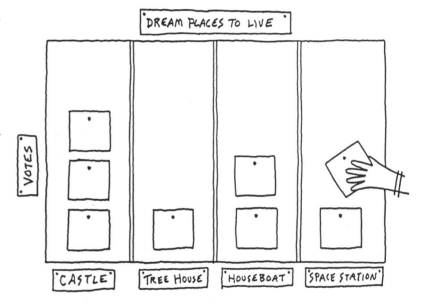

DATA DAZZLER

America's biggest home, Biltmore House in Asheville, North Carolina, has 250 rooms!

CHECK IT OUT!

Classify, count, and graph children's library books to analyze class reading preferences.

Materials
poster paper with grid lines drawn on it • markers

Here's What To Do
1. Brainstorm categories of books children like to read. List them on the chalkboard.

2. Visit the library. Follow the usual rules for taking out books. Tell the children that before any books go home, they'll examine the kinds of books they've checked out.

3. Back in the classroom, use the chalkboard list to make a class bar graph about library books. Have children help you to give the graph a title, label each axis, and put in a scale. Discuss how bars can show how many books of each kind were signed out.

4. Ask children to identify the category that best describes their book(s), such as science fiction, biography, mystery, picture book, or joke book. Then color a box in the appropriate row of the graph for each of their books.

Wrap It Up
◆ What does the bar graph show? What does it *not* show?

◆ Which category is most popular? Were any categories not used? Which ones?

◆ How many books did our class check out this week?

◆ How else can we keep track of the same data?

◆ If we added new book data each week, what do you think would happen to the graph?

And Then...
◆ Continue recording library book preferences on the bar graph for a month or even for the year. Don't be surprised if you have to add categories or extend the graph to accommodate other titles given by book lovers.

◆ As children learn about pictographs, you might have them rework the data in that form.

Tip
◆ For younger children, use fewer, simpler categories, such as fiction and nonfiction, or picture books and chapter books.

DATA DAZZLER
You think your community has a big library? It may, but the Library of Congress in Washington, D.C. has 532 miles of shelving for its enormous collection.

HERE, FIDO!

Children graph the number of syllables in pet names.

Materials
Teacher Resource Sheet or

Here's What To Do
1. Have each child list 12 names for pets, either names of real pets or names they'd like to use.
2. Ask the children to count and record the number of syllables in each name. They may clap the beats or say the names aloud, as needed.
3. Distribute ▼3 or ▼4. Help children customize the form to create a bar graph about syllables in their list of pet names. The graph might be called SYLLABLES IN PET NAMES. One axis might be labeled NUMBER OF SYLLABLES, with bars for 1, 2, 3, and 4, or more. The other might be labeled PET ANIMALS. Remind children to include a scale.
4. Have children complete the bar graph using their list of names.

Wrap It Up
◆ Among the pets you listed, how many have 1-syllable names? How many have 2-syllable names? 3-syllable names? Names with 4 or more syllables?
◆ Can you draw any conclusions about pet names from your data or from the data other people have? Explain.
◆ If you changed your dog's name to LaPhonso, how would the graph change?

And Then...
◆ Have children make a syllable graph for the names of the states in the United States.
◆ Some children may want to make a syllable graph for the last names of American presidents.
◆ Suggest that children make a syllable graph for words that mean "hello" in as many different languages as possible.

END TO END

Children measure with nonstandard units and graph their findings.

Materials

paper clips • chalk or crayons • drinking straws or new pencils • Teacher Resource Sheet or

Here's What To Do

1. Have children place paper clips end to end to measure the distance from the front edge of their desk to the back. Have them record the number of paper clips they used.

2. Next, have children use a unit that's longer than a paper clip, such as a crayon or piece of chalk, to measure the same length. Again, they record the number of units they used.

3. For a third measure, have children pick an even longer unit, such as a drinking straw or new pencil. As before, they measure and record the number of units.

4. Now help the children make a bar graph to show the data they've gathered. Each bar shows how many units equal the length of the desk from front to back. Provide copies of ▼3 or ▼4, customized to fit this data. Here's how it might look:

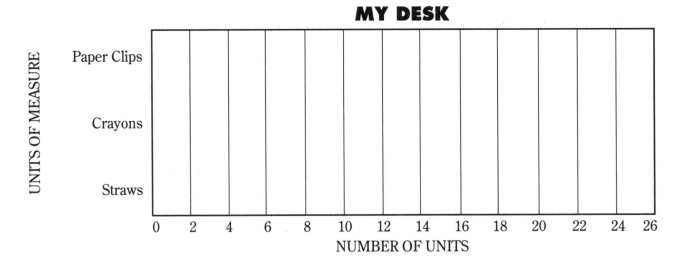

Wrap It Up

◆ How can the same length have so many different measurements?

◆ Suppose you measured the same distance in shoe lengths and added the data to your graph. Predict how the length of the bar would compare to the bars you've already got.

And Then...

Have children try some other trios of nonstandard measures, such as the following:

◆ the width of a bulletin board in staplers, shoes, and markers;

◆ the length of the room in arm spans, baseball bats, and umbrellas;

◆ the height of a bookcase in hand spans, dictionaries, and paintbrushes.

Tips

◆ If children sit at large or nonrectangular tables, choose another object they can measure, such as their seats.

◆ If a length isn't an exact number of units, children can pick the nearest whole unit.

FOLLOW THE BOUNCING BALL

Teams tally ball-game data and make a bar graph.

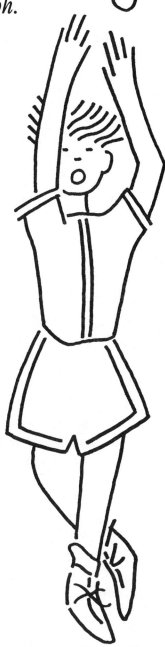

Materials
tennis balls or rubber balls • Teacher Resource Sheet **2**; **3** or **4**

Here's What To Do

1. Divide the class into teams of three. Give each team a ball. Tell them they're going to play a game and tally scores.

2. Here are the rules: Two children stand about 10 feet apart and bounce a ball back and forth between them. Only one bounce allowed. A third child tallies every time the ball is caught on one bounce. When a ball is dropped or bounces more than once, the round ends. Each team plays 6 rounds, keeping a separate tally each time. They can use **2** as a tally table. Have children rotate so that everyone gets to toss and tally.

3. When a team has completed 6 rounds, the players use the data they tallied to make a bar graph. Each bar represents the number of catches in one round. Teams can use **3** or **4** for the graphs. Remind teams to title the graph, label its sides, and pick a reasonable scale.

Wrap It Up

◆ How many bars does your graph have? Why? What labels did you use?

◆ How did you decide on a reasonable scale?

◆ In which round did your team catch the most balls? How many did you catch?

◆ How could you use your graph to compare your best and worst rounds?

◆ Suppose you saw another team's graph. How could you tell if their scores got better, stayed about the same, or got worse with each round?

And Then...
Children can tally and graph other catching or bouncing activities. They might count the number of times a ball thrown high into the air is caught or how many times teams can keep batting a volleyball back and forth before it hits the floor.

Tip
◆ **Vary the rules as necessary to suit children's skills. For example, children might stand farther apart or closer together, catch with one hand, or keep one eye closed.**

DATA DAZZLER
Some people have trouble holding on to one ball. But 16-year-old Travis Johnson of Missouri once held 9 baseballs in one hand without using tape or glue!

ON A ROLL

Children use graphing to explore probability and sharpen their understanding of chance.

Materials

pairs of number cubes • Teacher Resource Sheet **2**; **3** or **4**

Here's What To Do

1. Ask children what sums they can get by rolling a pair of number cubes. List all possible sums on the chalkboard. Then have children guess which sums they think will come up most often if they roll the number cubes 50 times. List these predictions.

2. Have children pair up. Give each pair a set of number cubes and **2** to use as a tally sheet. Have pairs copy the list of possible sums onto their sheet.

3. Now it's time to toss and tally. One partner rolls the cubes 25 times while the other tallies the sums. After 25 tallies, children switch roles for 25 more rolls.

4. When they finish rolling and tallying, pairs make a bar graph to show their results. Provide **3** or **4** for the graph. Remind children to give their graph a title, a scale, and labels so that others can read and understand the data shown.

5. Partners can post their graphs on the bulletin board. Have them compare their actual results with their earlier predictions.

Wrap It Up

◆ Look at all the graphs. Do you notice any patterns? Explain.

◆ Which sums came up most often? Least often?

◆ Why do you think this is so?

And Then...

Try a similar activity with spinners divided into three sections—two quarter sections and one half section. Ask children to predict the results for 80 spins. Then have them spin to get actual data to compare with their predictions. Have children tally and graph their totals.

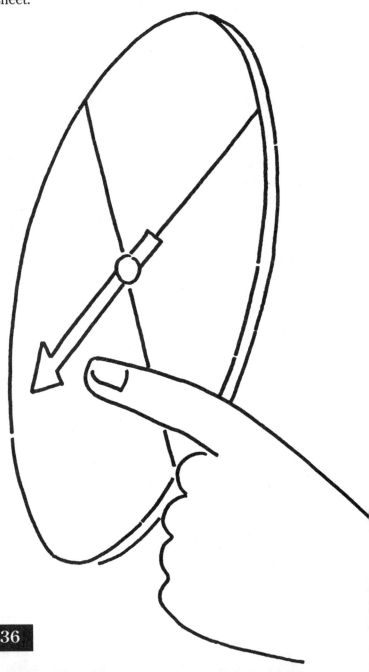

SPOT CHECK

Children collect data about TV commercials to display in a graph.

Materials
home letter (page 38) •
Teacher Resource Sheet **3** or **4**

Here's What To Do

1. Talk with the class about commercials. Be sure children understand that the purpose of any commercial is to get people to buy things.

2. Brainstorm a list of products that commercials try to sell, such as toys, cars, fast food, and medicine. Try to keep the list short and broad.

3. Duplicate and distribute the letter on page 38 to the children. Together, read the note to parents which explains the assignment. Answer any questions children may have. Invite them to copy the commercial categories from the class list onto the table. Or tell children to fill in the categories at home, based on whatever they see during their investigation.

4. Tomorrow, after you discuss the data, each child will use his or her tally table to make a bar graph to display the data. Provide copies of **3** or **4** for this activity.

Wrap It Up

◆ How many categories of commercials did you see?

◆ How many commercials did you see? Was the number more or less than you expected?

◆ Are there types of commercials everyone saw, no matter which show they watched?

◆ Would the data change if you watched on a different day or at another time? Explain.

And Then...

Try the Spot Check again during a Saturday morning cartoon show. Have children compare the results of both investigations.

Tip
◆ Explain that there are different types of commercials. Some ask you to watch other shows on that channel and others, called public service announcements (PSAs), provide useful information to the community.

DATA DAZZLER

The longest TV show lasted over 163 hours! In July 1969, an Australian TV station covered the Apollo XI mission, during which astronauts first walked on the moon.

Name _____

DEAR FAMILY MEMBERS,

For a math project, we're collecting data about television commercials. Please help your child by watching a 30-minute TV show together tonight. Start watching exactly when the show begins and watch until the next show starts to be sure to see every commercial that airs during the half-hour. Your child can use the table below to tally the number of commercials that air and the kinds of products they advertise.

Thanks for your help. Remind your child to bring the completed table to school tomorrow.

Name of show: _____

The show was on from _____ to _____.

KIND OF COMMERCIAL	TALLY

Total number of commercials I counted: _____

KERNEL OF AN IDEA

Guessing and checking translates into a double bar graph.

Children guess and check the number of popcorn kernels, then display the data in a double bar graph.

Materials

popped popcorn • measuring cups • paper plates • Teacher Resource Sheet **1**; **3** or **4**

Here's What To Do

1. Grab the biggest handful of popcorn you can hold in one hand. Ask the class to guess how many kernels you've got. Then take your own best guess and record it on the chalkboard in a table like this:

Name	Guess	Kernel Count

2. Dump your handful of popcorn onto a paper plate. Count the kernels. You'll have to account for broken and unpopped kernels. For example, you might count 4 broken kernels as 1 whole kernel or 3 unpopped kernels as 1 popped kernel. Record the actual count beside your estimate.

3. Demonstrate how to record the guess *and* the actual kernel count on a double bar graph. One bar shows the estimate and the other shows the actual count. Draw the bars next to one another, using a different color for each. Have children help you name the graph, label the sides, and choose a reasonable scale. Since this graph shows two bars for each person, you'll need a color (or pattern) key.

4. Divide the class into groups of 3. By turns, children grab, estimate, dump, and count the number of kernels in the biggest handful of popcorn they can hold. The group records each person's estimate and actual count on **1**, customized to show three columns. Then they show the data in a double bar graph. Provide **3** or **4** for the graph.

Wrap It Up

◆ How do the table and the graph go together?
◆ How is a double bar graph like any bar graph? How is it different?
◆ In your group, who made an estimate that was higher than the actual count? Lower? How does the graph show this?
◆ Who in your group made the closest estimate? How does the graph show this?
◆ Can you imagine another time when you might use a double bar graph? Explain.

And Then...

Try this activity again with other objects, such as foam-packing peanuts, pasta, or unattached snap cubes. Children grab, estimate, dump, and count, and then show their results in a double bar graph.

I CHART

Children measure, estimate, and graph body distances— including the width of their smile.

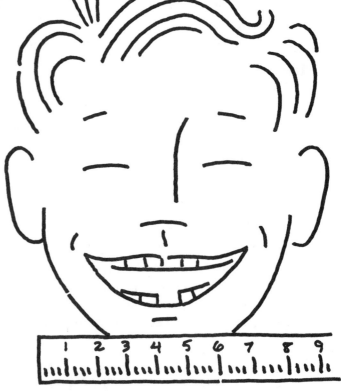

Materials
metric measuring tools (tape measures, rulers) • string • Dimension Data Table (page 41) • Teacher Resource Sheet ▼4

Here's What To Do
1. Ask children to guess how wide their smiles are. Talk about ways to measure a smile.

2. Divide the class into pairs. Distribute copies of the Dimension Data Table on page 41 to each pair. Read the entries on the table together. Discuss ways to take measurements that involve curves.

3. Have children first estimate the first body distance in centimeters and record that information on the table. Then they help each other measure their smile exactly and record that number. They continue through the table, first estimating and then measuring each body distance given.

4. Each child uses his or her own data to make a double bar graph. Provide copies of ▼4. For each body distance on the table, the graph should show a pair of bars that compare the estimate and the actual measure. Remind children to name their graph, label the sides, give a scale, and provide a key to distinguish between the two kinds of bars.

Wrap It Up
◆ Which body dimensions were greater than you estimated? Which were smaller? How does the graph show this?
◆ Which estimate was nearest to the actual size?
◆ Why is a double bar graph useful to show this kind of data?

And Then...
Have children estimate, measure, and graph other body distances, such as shin length, nose length, distance around the fist or funny bone, space between eyebrows, and so on.

DATA DAZZLER
Shridhar Chillal of India hasn't cut his fingernails since 1952. At last measure, his thumbnail was 40 inches long!

Tip
◆ Measure a curve by tracing it with string, then measuring the length of string used.

Name _____

DIMENSION DATA

Body Part	Estimate	Actual Measure
width of smile	cm	cm
length of thumbnail	cm	cm
distance around big toe	cm	cm
length of one eyebrow	cm	cm
distance around wrist	cm	cm
height of ear	cm	cm
length of jaw line from ear to ear	cm	cm

INTRODUCTION TO PICTOGRAPHS

While all graphs are visual by definition, pictographs offer children an especially appealing way to display data. Pictographs (sometimes known as picture graphs) rely on the use of a picture or symbol to represent a fixed quantity of data. The key to understanding and using a pictograph is to recognize the meaning of the symbol and its relationship to the data.

The pictograph activities that follow progress from the concrete to the abstract. They are organized to help children understand what a pictograph is, how to read a pictograph, how to design and construct one, and how to use a pictograph to display and interpret data. The first activity features a pictograph made with real objects. Then, as children learn that symbols can stand for amounts, they move on to create their own pictographs.

Look for reproducible pictograph activities in Part 2 on pages 77 through 79.

RELATED SKILLS
- number sense
- understanding and using tally marks
- making, using, and interpreting tables
- multiplying whole numbers (or skip-counting)

EVERY PICTOGRAPH HAS
- a title
- two columns
- picture symbols to represent data
- a key that shows the recurring symbol with its given value

FAST FACTS ABOUT PICTOGRAPHS
- One symbol can represent one item or many items.
- Within a pictograph, the symbol always has the same value.
- In most pictographs, the kinds of data are shown in the left column and the symbols representing the quantities of each are placed horizontally in the right column.
- Pictographs sometimes use fractional parts of symbols. For instance, if the symbol stands for 10 zebras, a half symbol stands for 5 zebras.

FIVE STEPS TO A PICTOGRAPH
1. Make a table with two columns—one for the kinds of data and one for the quantity of data. Label each column.

2. List all the things to compare in the left column.

3. Choose a picture to use as a symbol. Decide what quantity it represents, based on the data. Draw one symbol and its value in a key below the graph.

4. Draw the appropriate number of pictures in the right column of the graph.

5. Write a title above the graph.

Use the pictograph on the next page as a teaching tool. Copy it onto the chalkboard or chart paper, or make a transparency of it to use with an overhead projector.

FIREFLIES COUNTED IN BUGG PARK

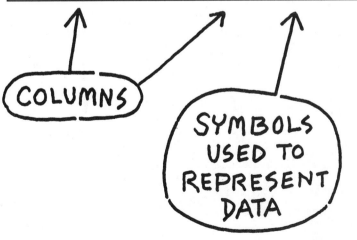

Monday	🔦 🔦
Tuesday	🔦 🔦 🔦 🔦
Wednesday	🔦 🔦
Thursday	🔦 🔦 🔦 🔦 🔦
Friday	🔦 🔦 🔦

COLUMNS

SYMBOLS USED TO REPRESENT DATA

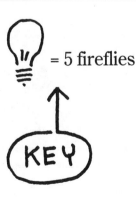

= 5 fireflies

KEY

FANCY FOOTWORK

Actual shoes form the basis for a pictograph that shows class footwear.

Materials
index cards • chart paper • paper foot shapes • tape or glue

Here's What To Do

1. Brainstorm ways to classify the kinds of shoes children have on today. Ideas may include shoes that slip on or ones that tie; fabric or leather shoes; shoes with laces, buckles, zippers, or Velcro; sneakers, boots, sandals, moccasins, or party shoes.

2. Write each category on an index card. Place the cards in a column in an open area of the classroom floor.

3. Ask children to take off one shoe and place it in a horizontal row to the right of the card that best describes it. When all shoes are in place, have a volunteer straighten the rows.

4. Talk about the shoe graph. Challenge children to think of ways to show the same data on paper. Some may suggest bar graphs or tally tables. Tell them about another kind of graph that uses pictures.

5. Together, make a class pictograph on chart paper for the shoes on the floor. List categories on the left and label the column KINDS OF SHOES. Use a foot shape to stand for a shoe. Write a key beneath the graph that says 1 foot =1 person's shoe. Give each child a foot shape to place on the row of the pictograph that corresponds to the row on the floor. Check that the pictograph matches the shoe graph by having children put their shoes back on once they've placed their picture on the graph.

Wrap It Up

◆ How does a pictograph work? How is it like a bar graph? How is it different?

◆ How does our pictograph show what we first showed with our shoes?

◆ What did the floor graph show about our shoes that the pictograph does *not* show?

◆ Which kind of shoe is most common in our class today? How can you tell?

◆ If we make another pictograph about our shoes tomorrow, how can we do it without taking them off?

And Then...
Make pictographs about other kinds of clothing, such as socks, outerwear, or shirts.

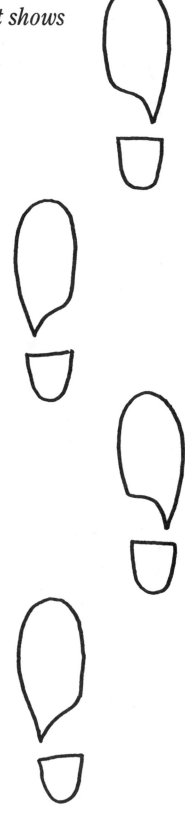

HIDE AND PEEK

This class pictograph presents data on favorite costumes.

Materials
chart paper • construction paper • scissors

Here's What To Do

1. Brainstorm a list of favorite costumes that the children would choose for a costume party or a Halloween parade.

2. Narrow the list to 4 to 6 kinds of costumes. Write those categories along the left edge of a piece of chart paper. Tell the children that they're going to vote for their favorite costume on a pictograph using a mask symbol. Give the pictograph a title, such as FAVORITE COSTUMES IN OUR CLASS. Label the left column COSTUMES and the right column VOTES. Write the key: 1 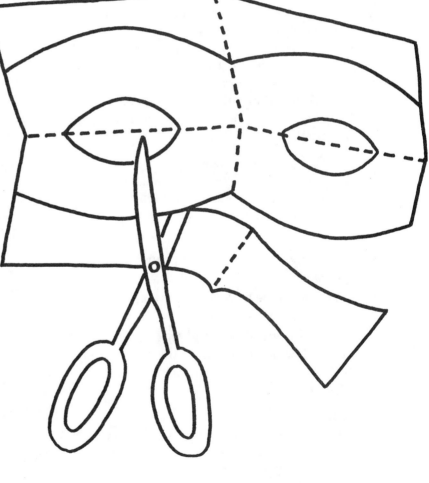 = 1 vote.

3. Distribute construction paper and scissors. Demonstrate how to cut out a symmetrical mask shape by folding the paper in fourths, cutting out eye holes, and unfolding it.

4. After children have made their masks, have them come to the pictograph and paste the masks in the row for their favorite costume. Be sure everyone casts one vote— even you!

Wrap It Up

◆ What is the key on this pictograph? Why is it important?

◆ Which costume is the favorite in our class? How does the pictograph show this?

◆ How many children voted for witch? For ghost? For cat? (Substitute categories as needed.)

◆ How can we tell how many kids voted in all?

◆ How can we make a pictograph for this data without paper mask shapes?

And Then...
Gather more data for the pictograph by talking to children in other classes. Add the data using the existing key. Then discuss how to adjust the key so the graph could have fewer pictures but still show the same data. (Hint: Let 1 ⬤ = 2 votes.)

CURRENCY EVENTS

Children create their own symbol to use in a pictograph showing prices of classroom objects.

Materials

classroom items labeled with price tags • Teacher Resource Sheet  5 • play coins

Here's What To Do

1. Before class, label 5 objects with prices that are multiples of 5. For instance, you might show a ruler for 25¢, an eraser for 10¢, a marker for 20¢, a pad for 35¢, and a roll of tape for 40¢. Display the objects where everyone can see them.

2. Have children list the names of the items on 5, then model each price with play coins.

3. Compare the combinations of coins that the children used to show each price. Explain that a pictograph can have only one kind of picture. Talk about how to choose. Children may want to use a picture of a penny or a nickel, but challenge them to think of a picture that does not look like a coin. You might suggest a picture of a price tag, with the key: 1 $ = 5¢.

4. Have children make their own price symbols for the objects. Remind them to include in their pictograph a title, labels for the columns, the key, and as many pictures per row as necessary.

Wrap It Up

◆ How would you explain your pictograph to someone?

◆ Why would it be a problem to use a symbol that stood for 25¢ or $1?

◆ What if the prices were higher, such as $1.25 or $2.50? How would your pictograph look? Would you think of a different value for the symbol? Like what?

And Then...

Use real price lists, catalogs, or flyers as a basis for other pictographs. Pairs can work together to select items, a symbol, a reasonable value for the symbol, and then make price pictographs to hang up in the class.

DATA DAZZLER

In 1985, volunteers for the National Kidney Foundation in Atlanta, Georgia, made a line of 663,152 quarters that stretched for over 10 miles! It was worth $165,788.

46

DATASAURUS

The class uses a chart of dinosaur lengths as data for a group pictograph.

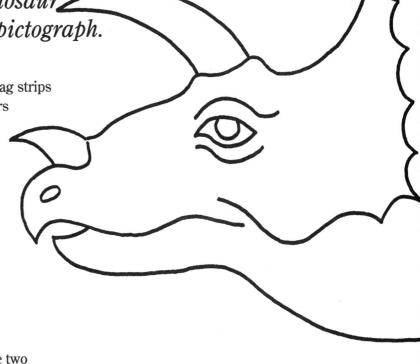

Materials
chart of dinosaur lengths (page 48) • oaktag strips (about 3 x 18 inches) • crayons or markers

Here's What To Do

1. Clear an area on a bulletin board or classroom wall. Explain that everyone will contribute to a large pictograph showing data of dinosaur sizes.

2. Duplicate the table on page 48 and distribute it. Read and discuss the data together.

3. Have children agree on a title for the dinosaur pictograph and pick a symbol that's easy to draw, such as a footprint, bone, or dinosaur body shape. Label the two columns KIND OF DINOSAUR and LENGTH. Write the names of the dinosaurs in the left-hand column. With the children, determine a value for the symbol and make a key.

4. Give each child an oaktag strip and the name of a dinosaur from the list. Each oaktag strip will become a row of data for a dinosaur. Children draw the appropriate number of symbols for the length of their dinosaur on the strip. As they finish, they attach the strip to the pictograph next to their dinosaur.

Wrap It Up

◆ How can we check that each row has the correct number of symbols?

◆ How can you identify dinosaurs that were the same length?

◆ What if scientists discover a new dinosaur that was 120 feet long. How would we show this on our pictograph?

Tips
◆ Given the range of lengths, choosing a reasonable value for the symbol may be difficult for children. Guide them to select a large enough value so that the graph is manageable. Tell them that they may estimate or round some data.

◆ Agree upon a size for the symbols. If a child's drawings are much too large or small, they may have to be redrawn.

DATA DAZZLER

Before Godzilla or Dino of TV's *The Flintstones*, there was Gertie. Created in 1912 by Winsor McCay, Gertie, an animated cartoon, was the first-ever movie dinosaur.

DINOSAUR	Length
Adasaurus	7 ft
Alamosaurus	65 ft
Albertosaurus	26 ft
Allosaurus	36 ft
Apatosaurus	70 ft
Bactrosaurus	18 ft
Barosaurus	90 ft
Camarasaurus	55 ft
Ceratosaurus	18 ft
Coelophysis	10 ft
Deinonychus	10 ft
Diplodocus	87 ft
Dravidosaurus	10 ft
Dryosaurus	12 ft
Edmontosaurus	42 ft
Eucentrosaurus	20 ft
Fabrosaurus	3 ft
Gasosaurus	13 ft
Hadrosaurus	30 ft
Herrerasaurus	10 ft
Hyspelosaurus	40 ft
Kakuru	8 ft
Kentrosaurus	17 ft
Kritosaurus	30 ft
Maiasaura	30 ft
Mamenchisaurus	89 ft
Marshosaurus	16 ft
Minmi	7 ft
Nanotyrannus	16 ft
Ultrasaurus	82 ft

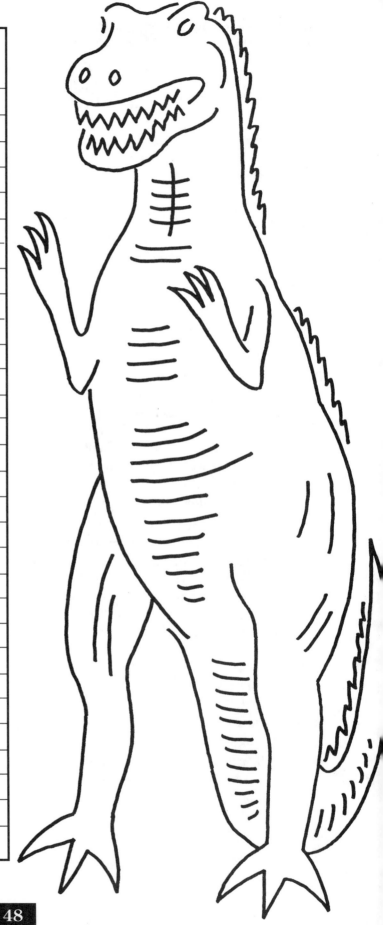

PIZZOLOGY

Pizza-topping preferences are presented in this pictograph.

Materials
chart paper • Teacher Resource Sheet 5

Here's What To Do

1. Brainstorm pizza toppings children like—peppers, onions, pepperoni, extra cheese, and so on—and list them on the chalkboard. Tally favorites as children identify the topping they like best.

2. Use the data to make a class pictograph on chart paper. Choose an easy-to-draw, easy-to-recognize symbol, such as a pizza slice or a pizza box.

3. Talk about what the graph shows. Ask children if they think they'd get similar results if they surveyed other children and grownups outside of class.

4. Have each child survey 20 people to find out their favorite pizza topping. Children should prepare a list of toppings in advance and use it to tally responses. They may add other toppings as people suggest them, but the list should not exceed 8 toppings. Allow 2 to 3 days for children to complete their surveys.

5. In class, have each child display the data in a pictograph using 5. Remind children to include a title, labels, and a key in their pictograph.

Wrap It Up

◆ What do all the pizza pictographs have in common?

◆ How do favorite pizza toppings outside of class compare with class favorites?

◆ How could you change the look of a pictograph without changing the data it shows?

And Then...
Top off the activity with a class pizza party!

Tips

◆ Discuss the importance of choosing a symbol that fits the data.

◆ If the symbol stands for more than 1 vote, talk about how to show *only* 1 vote.

DATA DAZZLER

The world's largest pizza, made in Singapore in 1990, was over 111 feet across!

THE WRITE STUFF

Children take a survey of preferred writing implements and graph the results.

Materials
Teacher Resource Sheet **2** and **5**

Here's What To Do

1. Brainstorm a list of writing implements children like to use, such as regular pencils, mechanical pencils, crayons, markers, and ballpoint pens.

2. Have children pair up. Distribute copies of **2** so pairs can record the list of writing implements the class generated. Each pair surveys at least 25 children in the school to find out which one they like to write with most.

3. After pairs gather their data, give them **5** to make a pictograph that shows the results of their survey. Have children choose a title and headings they like.

4. Discuss what pictures to use as symbols. An ink bottle might work or a page with lines on it. Remind children to pick a value for the symbol that fits their data.

5. Display all pictographs for class inspection and discussion.

Wrap It Up

◆ What symbol did you use? How many votes does it stand for?

◆ How can you tell by looking at a pictograph how many people were surveyed?

◆ Which graphs show similar results? Which show results that are very different? How can you explain the similarities and differences?

◆ What do *you* like to write with the most?

Tip

◆ You might assign each pair a different class to survey. This way, children can combine results into one big pictograph that represents the preferences of a large group.

DATA DAZZLER

About 140 years ago the pencil took a giant leap forward when Philadelphia's Hyman Lipman first attached an eraser to one by means of a small metal band. Thank Mr. Lipman the next time you fix a misspelled word.

CHECKS ON THE MAIL

Children record what kinds of mail their families get and graph the data.

Materials

Teacher Resource Sheet ▼**2** and ▼**5**

Here's What To Do

1. Tell children they're going to keep track for a week of the kinds of mail their families get and then make pictographs for a clear look at the data.

2. With the children's help, make a list of categories of mail. Try to keep the categories broad enough to have a manageable number of them. Have children copy the list onto ▼**2** and take it home with them.

3. Every day for a week, children tally the kinds of mail delivered to their home—letters, magazines, postcards, packages, junk mail, and so on. Tell children that they may adjust the categories in their tally table to match the mail, as necessary.

4. When the week is up, have each child display the results of the mail research in a pictograph. They can use ▼**5**. Suggest an envelope as a symbol. Have children pick a value for the envelope that makes sense for their data. Remind them that a symbol can stand for several pieces of mail, such as 3, 5, or 10 pieces.

5. When children finish, have them share their postal data with the class.

Wrap It Up

◆ What have we learned about our mail? Are there any surprises?

◆ Did our symbols represent the same number of items of mail? Explain.

◆ How did we adjust our categories at home? Why?

◆ How are pictographs useful for showing the results of our research?

◆ How can we use a bar graph to show the same data?

INTRODUCTION TO COORDINATE GRIDS

Simply put, a coordinate grid is a map. It's a useful tool for solving problems, particularly those that involve geometry and spatial concepts. Guide children to recognize coordinate grids in the world around them, such as the rows of seats in a movie theater or the grid of city streets.

The activities in this section begin with concrete experiences in which children move around on a large grid on the classroom floor. Then they use pencil and grid paper to plot and identify points using ordered pairs and to play strategy games. All the activities are designed to help children appreciate the orderly sequence and patterns of coordinate geometry.

Look for reproducible coordinate grid activities in Part 2 on pages 80 and 81.

RELATED SKILLS
- one-to-one correspondence
- counting
- left/right and horizontal/vertical directionality

EVERY COORDINATE GRID HAS
- two axes
- horizontal and vertical grid lines that intersect

FAST FACTS ABOUT THE COORDINATE GRID
- A coordinate grid is formed by the intersection of a horizontal and a vertical axis. The point of intersection is called the *origin*.

- Each point on the grid is named by an ordered pair of numbers known as *coordinates*. The number pair is written in parentheses; a comma separates the coordinates.
- For each point, the first coordinate gives the number of units *to the right* of the origin. The second coordinate gives the number of units *up* from there. For example, (5,2) names a point 5 units to the right and 2 units up from the origin, or 5 ACROSS, 2 UP.
- The coordinates of the origin are (0,0).

FOUR STEPS TO A COORDINATE GRID
1. Draw the two axes.

2. Label points along the axes, counting from the origin to the right along the horizontal axis and up along the vertical axis. Label as many points as necessary.

3. To locate a point, begin at the origin. Count *across* to the first coordinate in the ordered pair. From that point, count *up* the number of units given by the second coordinate.

4. To name a point, begin at the origin. Find the position on the horizontal axis directly below the point and record that number as the first coordinate. From there, count *up* to the point and record the number of units as the second coordinate.

Use the coordinate grid on the next page as a teaching tool. Copy it onto the chalkboard or chart paper, or make a transparency of it to use with an overhead projector.

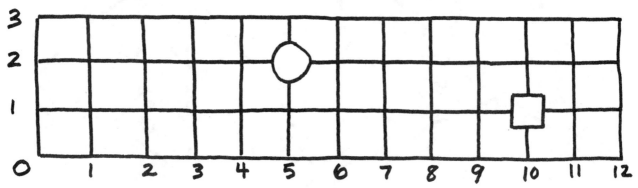

DESERT MAP

VERTICAL AXIS

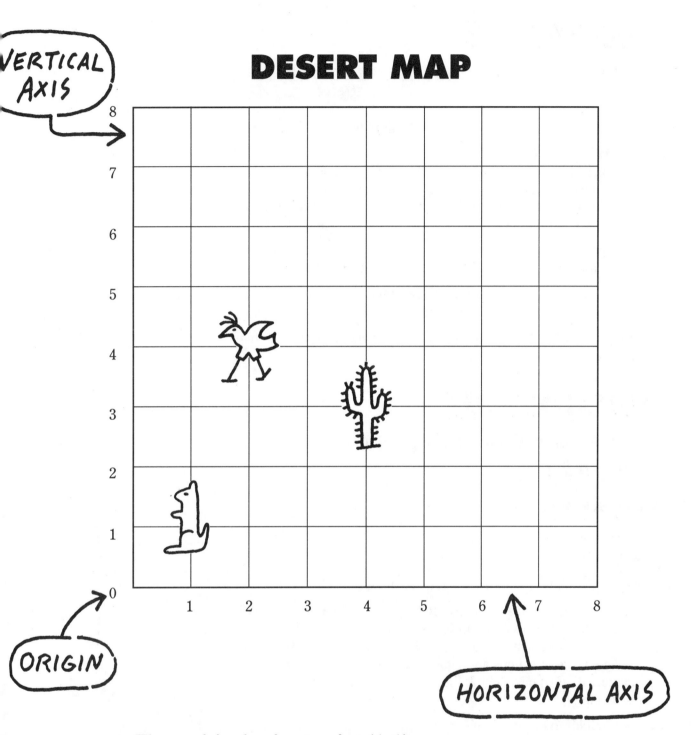

ORIGIN

HORIZONTAL AXIS

The prairie dog is at point (1,1).

The roadrunner is at point (2,4).

The cactus is at point (4,3).

GROUNDED

The floor is a firm foundation in coordinate graphing.

Materials
masking tape • red and green markers • large floor mat (see page 7) • index cards

Here's What To Do

1. Using masking tape, lay out horizontal and vertical grid lines on the classroom floor to represent a coordinate grid. If your floor is covered with square tiles, use them to make your grid. (If you have colored tape, indicate the axes in a different color from the other grid lines.) Make the grid large enough so children can walk on it from point to point and can stand on the intersections of grid lines.

2. Number the axes, using red for numbers on the horizontal axis and green for those on the vertical axis. Draw a large star on the origin (0,0) to indicate that it's a special place on the grid.

3. Examine the grid with your class. Guide children to notice that the same numbers appear on each axis and that they increase as you move away from the origin.

Please note: You may want to leave the masking-tape grid on the classroom floor as it is used in several of the activities that follow.

WALKABOUT

Children move to points along the grid according to directions given by a leader.

Here's What To Do

1. Explain these rules:

   • Always start at the star (the origin).

   • Always walk OVER across the red axis first, then UP.

2. Give directions such as, "Go OVER 3 and UP 2." To respond, a child starts at the origin, walks 3 units along the horizontal axis to the line labeled 3, pivots to the left on that point, and then walks 2 units up the line. If the directions are followed correctly, the child will be standing on the point (3,2). If there is a mistake, classmates can offer help.

3. When children become familiar with the grid system, they can give directions to each other. Challenge the children by encouraging them to add conditions to their directions. For example, children can direct classmates to points

   • that are near (or far from) the origin;

   • that form rows of children;

   • named by even numbers;

   • you can get to in 10 steps or less.

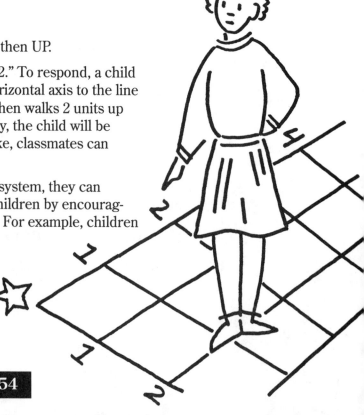

TREASURE HUNT

In this game, children name coordinates to claim objects you've placed on the grid.

Here's What To Do

1. Scatter a number of objects ("treasures") on the floor grid, each on its own point.

2. Children claim their favorite treasure by naming the point on which it can be found. The "address" of a treasure is an ordered pair. If a point is named correctly, the child can claim the treasure. If not, allow another turn or allow classmates to offer help.

3. After children become adept at Treasure Hunt, add conditions such as the following:

   • You can only claim an object whose coordinates add up to 7 (or 5, 10, etc.).

   • You can only claim an object that's in the same row (or column) as on another.

4. To extend the activity, challenge children to place the treasures themselves and make a treasure map that indicates each object's location. Children can use ▼**6** for the map.

PEANUT BUTTER AND JAM

Here's a game that also provides a way to form random partners.

Here's What To Do

1. Make a set of coordinate cards, enough for one card for every two children. Each card has an ordered pair that names a point on the grid. Now make a duplicate deck so that every point appears on two cards. Tell the class that you've made two identical decks.

2. Divide the class in half—one group is Peanut Butter, the other is Jam. Give each Peanut Butter member a coordinate card from one set, which the player must *not* show to anyone else. At a signal, Peanut Butters move onto the grid to the points named on their cards.

3. Explain that you will be handing out coordinate cards from the matching set to the Jam group to see which Peanut Butters and Jams go together (that is, which players have cards that name the same point). Before the Jams get their cards, they might enjoy guessing who they think their Peanut Butter partner might be.

4. Give the Jams their coordinate cards. They check their guesses by locating their point and seeing who's standing on it. If partners fail to find each other, have them double check their coordinates.

5. Children may enjoy tallying how many correct guesses (if any) there were.

6. As a variation, Jams can reveal information about their partners as a guessing game. For example, a Jam member might say—:

   • My Peanut Butter partner is near the origin.

   • My partner is at a point whose coordinates add up to 6.

   • My partner is at a point whose coordinates have a difference of 2.

   • My partner is at a point named by coordinate "twins" [(2,2), (5,5), etc.].

CONTROL TOWER

This movement game combines a floor grid and spatial reasoning to present a realistic application of coordinates.

Materials
floor grid • index cards

Here's What To Do

1. Talk about the job of air traffic controllers who direct airplanes to land and take off safely.

2. Lay out the floor grid. Place a sign that says AIRPORT at the point in the upper right corner of the grid.

3. Six children pretend to be airplanes. They can stand anywhere on the grid except at the airport.

4. Pairs of children pretend to be air traffic controllers. They must decide how to get the 6 planes safely to the airport without any accidents. Controllers plan clear "flight paths" by telling the planes to move from wherever they are to the airport according to the usual rules—OVER, then UP.

5. Have children take turns being planes and traffic controllers.

Wrap It Up

◆ How did you move the planes from where they were to the airport?

◆ How did you decide on an order for landing the planes?

◆ What might happen if you move the planes in a different order?

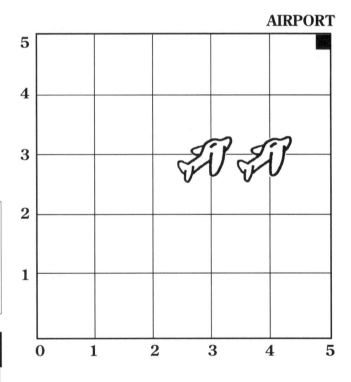

Tip
◆ On the grid shown, the plane at (4,3) must land to clear a flight path for the plane at (3,3).

FOUR IN A ROW

In this strategy game, children locate points on a coordinate grid.

Materials

Teacher Resource Sheet

Here's What To Do

1. Have children form groups of three. Give each group several copies of ⑥.

2. Explain the object of the game: To mark 4 points in a row, horizontally, vertically, or diagonally. The first player to do so wins.

3. Give the rules:

    • Two children, Player X and Player O, take turns to mark points on the grid.

    • In order to mark a point, a player must indicate it with the tip of a pencil and identify the coordinates (ordered pair) that name it.

    • The third person acts as Judge to determine whether the point has been named correctly. If so, the player can claim the point by making an X or O on it.

    • If a player misnames a point, no mark is made and the player loses that turn.

    • Children take turns playing and judging.

4. Tell children that Four in a Row takes strategy. They may need to plan ahead to block each other's moves. Help them see similarities between this game and Tic-Tac-Toe.

Present the illustrated situation so children can consider Player O's options.

And Then...

Suggest variations of the game:

◆ Change the goal to 3 or 5 points in a row.
◆ Have three people play at once—X, O, and P.
◆ Change the goal from making a row to making a box.

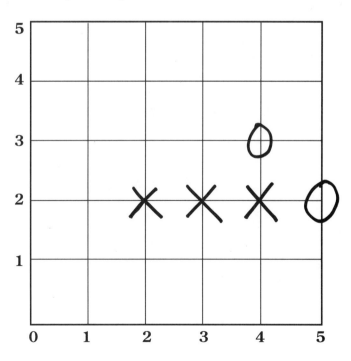

DATA DAZZLER

In 1989, 1,631 players, using a game board 2,090 feet long, played the world's biggest board game—a variation of the game Goose. Do you know a normal size of Goose?

GET THE POINT?

In this pair game, children follow oral directions to re-create their partner's drawing.

Materials

Teacher Resource

Here's What To Do

1. Have children pair up. Give each child a copy of ❻.

2. Have one child draw a simple, closed shape on his or her grid by connecting points with straight lines. The other child must *not* see this drawing.

3. To guide the other child to recreate the shape, the artist slowly names the points in the order in which they are connected. For instance, the artist might say: "Start at (3,3). Then go to (4,6). Now go to (1,6). Next..." As the artist names the points, the listener plots and connects them, point by point on his or her grid. After all points have been named, drawn, and connected in order, partners compare drawings to see if they match.

4. Have pairs talk about where they went wrong if the shapes don't match. Then they switch roles. Have them repeat the activity several times.

Wrap It Up

◆ What was hard about being the artist? What was hard about being the listener? Which did you prefer to be?

◆ Did you get better with practice?

DATA DAZZLER

The Battle of Gettysburg is one of the largest paintings in the world. It's 410 feet long and 70 feet high! You can see it at the National Military Park in Gettysburg, Pennsylvania.

FERRET IT OUT

Pairs play a game to locate a hidden ferret by making educated guesses on a coordinate grid.

Materials
Teacher Resource Sheet

Here's What To Do

1. Divide the class into pairs. Each child needs a copy of .

2. Explain these rules:

   • The goal is to locate the hidden ferret as fast as possible.

   • One child is the HIDER, the other is the FINDER. The HIDER makes a row of 4 points horizontally, vertically, or diagonally on his or her coordinate grid but does not show this secret row to the FINDER. This secret row is the FERRET.

   • The FINDER looks for the FERRET by naming points on the grid, one at a time. The HIDER says *yes* or *no* to tell whether a point named is in the secret row.

   • If a point is not on the FERRET, the FINDER keeps guessing until he or she names a point that *is* on the FERRET. Once a FERRET point is found, the FINDER has a clue to the location of the rest of the FERRET. The FINDER uses strategy to name the other points that mark the whole FERRET.

3. The FINDER uses his or her own grid to keep track of guesses. This will help the FINDER plan better guesses and avoid repeating points.

4. Have pairs take turns as FINDER and HIDER.

Wrap It Up
◆ Does one strategy work better than another to find the FERRET fast? Explain.
◆ How does luck play a part in this game?
◆ Would the game be easier or harder if the FERRET were a different size? Explain.

And Then...
Alter the rules of the game. For example:
◆ Have the HIDER give clues like "You're getting warmer" or "You have one of the coordinates right, but not the other."
◆ Change the size or shape of the FERRET.
◆ Have one HIDER and several FINDERS.
◆ Play with a different sized grid.

INTRODUCTION TO LINE GRAPHS

Most children have probably seen line graphs—they even turn up on cartoons. Line graphs show change over time. They can reveal broad trends or general tendencies as well as specific bits of data.

Like coordinate graphs, line graphs are based on the principle that two lines intersect at one point. A point on a line graph represents the place where two number scales meet.

The line graphing activities that follow progress from the concrete to the abstract. They are organized to help children understand what a line graph is, how to read a line graph, how to design and construct one, and how to use a line graph to display and interpret data. Children will gather data to make their own line graphs.

Look for reproducible line graph activities in Part 2 on pages 82 through 86.

RELATED SKILLS
◆ counting, comparing, and recognizing numbers
◆ making, using, and interpreting tables
◆ understanding and using a coordinate grid

EVERY LINE GRAPH HAS
◆ a title
◆ two sides (the vertical and horizontal axes)
◆ descriptive labels for each side (or axis)
◆ a scale calibrated to suit the data (by 1s, 2s, 5s, 10s, 25s, etc.)

FAST FACTS ABOUT LINE GRAPHS
◆ Points on a line graph are connected by line segments.
◆ A sloping segment indicates change; the steeper the slope, the greater the change.
◆ From left to right, a rise indicates increase; a downward slope indicates decrease.
◆ A horizontal (or flat) line segment indicates no change.

FIVE STEPS TO A LINE GRAPH
1. Draw and label the vertical and horizontal sides (axes).
2. Choose a scale that suits the data.
3. Place dots on the graph to represent the data.
4. Connect the dots in order.
5. Write a title above the graph.

Use the line graph on the next page as a teaching tool. Copy it onto the chalkboard or chart paper, or make a transparency of it to use with an overhead projector.

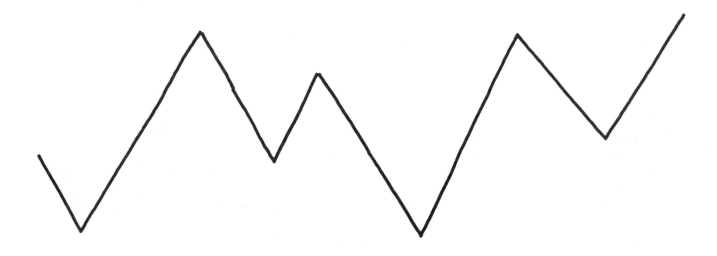

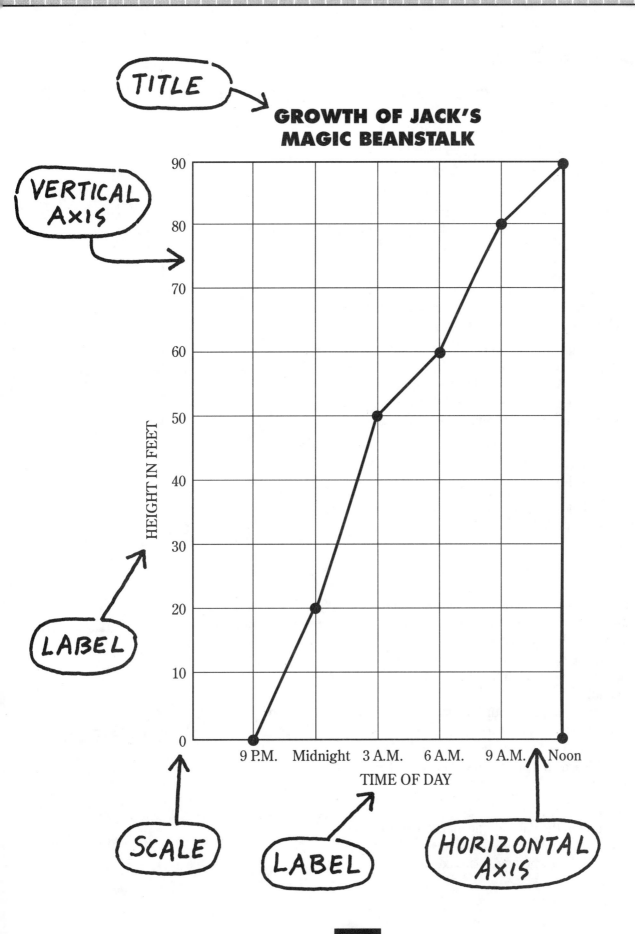

TITLE

GROWTH OF JACK'S
MAGIC BEANSTALK

VERTICAL AXIS

LABEL

HEIGHT IN FEET

90
80
70
60
50
40
30
20
10
0

9 P.M.　Midnight　3 A.M.　6 A.M.　9 A.M.　Noon

TIME OF DAY

SCALE

LABEL

HORIZONTAL AXIS

ROLL CALL

A line graph helps children keep track of daily attendance.

Materials
paper strips (or poster paper) • pushpins • yarn

Here's What To Do

1. Set up for this activity by making a coordinate grid on a bulletin board. Use strips of paper for grid lines, or draw the grid on poster paper and tack it up. Title the graph ATTENDANCE. Label the horizontal axis DAYS OF THE WEEK and indicate the lines that represent each day, Monday through Friday. Label the vertical axis NUMBER OF KIDS and calibrate it to fit the number of children in your class.

2. Talk with the class about how you usually record daily attendance. Then tell them that you're going to show attendance in a new way, on a line graph.

3. After you take attendance on Monday, have a volunteer find the line for Monday. Then have another child find the number on the vertical axis that equals the number of children in attendance that day. Demonstrate where the lines intersect and place a pushpin there.

4. Each day for the rest of the week, locate the point for the day's attendance on the graph and attach a pushpin to show it.

5. At the end of the week, stretch yarn from point to point to complete the line graph.

Wrap It Up
- What does the line on our graph show?
- On which day were the most children in class? How does the line graph show this?
- What would you say to a friend to explain how to read the line graph?
- What will next week's line graph look like if a lot of children catch the flu over the weekend?
- What would happen to our line graph if we added data about Saturday attendance?
- What can you tell about attendance if the line slants upward? If it slants downward? If it has no slant?

And Then...
Try a variation of the daily attendance line graph by showing the number of children absent or the number of children who have planned after-school events.

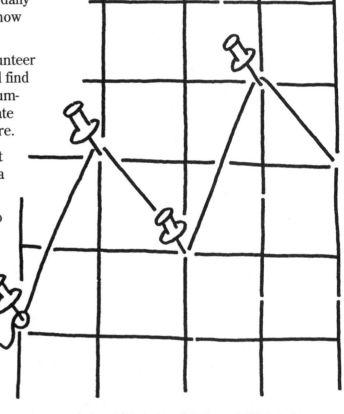

DATA DAZZLER
It must have been hard to keep track of attendance for Wilma Williams. Between 1933 and 1943 she went to 265 schools because her parents were traveling performers.

SUNNY SIDE UP

In this line graph activity, children display data on sunrise times in your area.

Materials
chart paper • yellow marker or paper circles (optional) • Teacher Resource Sheet **7** (optional)

Here's What To Do
1. Tell the class that you're going to work together to make a graph that shows when the sun rises each day for a month.

2. Make a large grid on chart paper. Call it SUNRISE TIMES THIS MONTH. Label the horizontal axis DATES, and fill in the dates for the month. Label the vertical axis TIMES, and calibrate it by minutes based on a reasonable range of sunrise times for your area and time of year.

3. On the first day you record data, find the exact time of sunrise. Show children how to find this fact in the local paper, or tell them when to hear it on TV or radio. Find the point that represents the sunrise time and draw a large dot there.

4. The next day, draw a large dot to indicate the day's sunrise time. Connect the two points with a line. Continue adding data throughout the month. You might have volunteers help you, or pick a different child to be responsible for adding the data each day.

Wrap It Up

◆ What pattern does the line graph show?
◆ According to our graph, when was the earliest (or latest) sunrise?
◆ About how many minutes later (or earlier) did the sun rise on one day than on the day before? Was this the same amount of time every day?
◆ Suppose we forgot to record the sunrise time on the 7th, but we did record the times for the 6th and the 8th. How could we use the graph to estimate the unknown time?
◆ If we continue the line graph for another month, how do you think it will look?

And Then...
Try a similar class graph for sunset times. Compare both graphs to look for patterns. Or have children make their own line graphs on **7** to show sunset data for a week.

DATA DAZZLER

Scientists count 182 days a year when the sun doesn't shine at all on the South Pole, and 176 days when there's no sunshine on the North Pole.

Tip
◆ Use a yellow highlighting marker to draw the dots, or attach small yellow paper circles to emphasize the plotting of a point for each piece of data.

ON BALANCE

In this activity, children graph their progress in learning a new task.

Materials
pencils • stopwatch or clock with a second hand • Teacher Resource Sheet ▼7

Here's What To Do

1. Talk about the saying "Practice makes perfect." Tell children that they're going to try a task and practice it to see if they get better at it.

2. Have a child time you (in seconds) to see how long it takes you to balance a pencil on your finger, seesaw-style. Record this data in a table on the chalkboard. Label the columns ATTEMPT and TIME. Repeat the task twice more, and record your times. After the third attempt, talk about whether you got better, worse, or stayed the same.

3. Show the pencil-balancing data in a line graph. Discuss suitable titles, labels for the axes, and a reasonable scale to use for the time.

4. Divide the class into groups of 3. One child is the Timer, one is the Balancer, and one is the Recorder, who keeps track of the data. Have each child make 7 timed attempts to balance a pencil on his or her finger. Children should rotate jobs so that everyone balances, times, and records.

5. After the trials, give each child ▼7 to make a line graph of his or her own data. Remind children to give their graphs a title, label the axes, and use a reasonable scale. Encourage group members to help each other. Display the completed graphs.

Wrap It Up
◆ Why is a line graph a good way to show this kind of data?
◆ How many points did you plot on your graph? Why?
◆ Why do some line graphs show ups and downs, while others show a steady slant in one direction?
◆ How could you describe what a flat line means on a graph for this activity?

And Then...
Graph the learning curve for other tasks, such as timed number facts quizzes, sports skills, or anything else children suggest.

DATA DAZZLER

You could probably learn to balance a spinning plate on the end of stick. But in 1986, Dave Spathaky managed to get 84 plates spinning—all at the same time!

SEEING DOUBLE

Children tally the number of trials it takes to roll a double with a set of number cubes, then show the data in a line graph.

Materials
pairs of number cubes • Teacher Resource Sheet  **2** and **7**

Here's What To Do

1. Divide the class into pairs. Give each pair two number cubes and **2**.

2. One partner begins as Roller, the other as Recorder. The Roller rolls the cubes as many times as necessary until a double appears. The Recorder tallies how many rolls it took to reach the double. Call this group of rolls a *set*. Be sure children understand that a set may be made up of many rolls or as few as one, if a double comes up right away.

3. Children switch jobs and repeat the activity, continuing until each partner completes 7 sets.

4. Give each child **7** to make a line graph for his or her data. Pairs can help each other decide on a descriptive title, clear labels for the axes, and a suitable scale. Remind them to connect all the points in order.

Wrap It Up

◆ How many points did you plot on your line graph? Why?

◆ What was the fewest number of rolls you had in any one set? The greatest number?

◆ How did you decide on your scale? Why might some graphs have different scales?

◆ Why do you think so many graphs show ups and downs?

◆ Can you learn to be better at rolling a double? Explain.

And Then...
Try other activities in which children tally the number of trials it takes to reach a specific outcome, such as rolling a target number, landing on a particular color or number on a spinner, or drawing a given color from a bag of assorted cubes without looking. Have children show the results in line graph form.

A MATTER OF DEGREES

Children graph weather data in various locations.

Materials
Teacher Resource Sheet **7** • weather data on high temperatures in other cities • wall map (optional)

Here's What To Do

1. Display some newspaper pages that give data about the high temperatures in cities around the nation or world. Help children read the tables or charts.

2. Assign each child a different city in the nation or the world. You might indicate the cities the class has chosen on a map or chart.

3. Have children follow their city's high temperature every day for 10 days. They can record the data in a table.

4. After they gather data about their city, children can use **7** to make a line graph that shows the pattern of high temperatures during the investigation. Remind them to give their graph a title, label the axes, use a reasonable scale, and connect all points.

Tip
◆ If children collect all data before they make their graphs, they'll have a better sense of the range of numbers they'll need on their scale.

DATA DAZZLER

On July 10, 1913, Death Valley, California recorded the hottest temperature ever in the United States. On that blistering day, the mercury hit a dizzying 134°!

Wrap It Up
Display the line graphs around the room.
◆ How could you find two cities that had similar temperatures during this time?
◆ Of all the cities we investigated, which had the highest high temperature? The lowest?
◆ Which city had high temperatures that changed the least during this time? How does the graph show this?
◆ Which city had the greatest change in temperature? What does its graph look like?
◆ Did any city experience a steady rise (or drop) in temperatures? How can you tell?

And Then...
Repeat the investigation for daily low temperatures in the same cities.

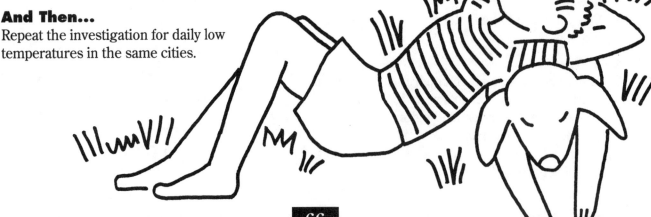

Part 2

Reproducible Student Pages: Interpreting Data

USING THESE PAGES

Part 2 contains 18 reproducible student pages to supplement the activities in Part 1. They are organized by graph type. You can use them in class, make them available in math center work stations, or assign them for homework. The answers for these graphing activities appear on pages 87 and 88.

Here's what you'll find:

Topic	Pages
Tables	69–70
Bar Graphs	71–76
Pictographs	77–79
Coordinate Grids	80–81
Line Graphs	82–86

MIXED-UP MORNING

It's the day after the town fair. Meg asks her friends which rides they liked best. She tallies the results and makes a table. Meg finds that most kids loved the Zoom-O-Coaster best. As many kids liked the Bouncing Bunny Bump as the Flying Frog. Three kids liked the Giggle Wheel most.

The parts of Meg's table are shown below. But they are all mixed up. Cut out all the parts. Then glue them on a sheet of paper to form a table. Be sure it makes sense. Does it fit the facts?

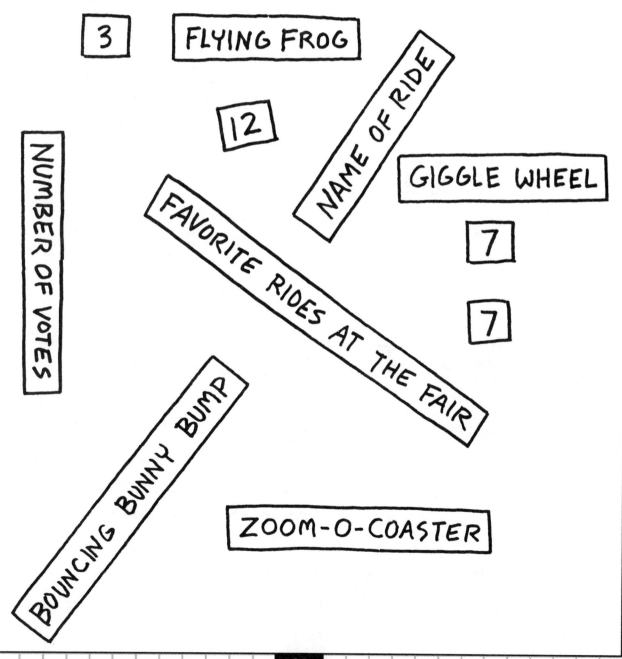

TABLE TALK

You can show the same data in different ways. Sometimes one way is more helpful than another. It all depends on what you want to know.

Nate took a survey in his class. He asked kids to name the animal with the biggest ears. First he collected his data. Then he displayed it two ways.

Look at Nate's tables. They show the same information. Then answer the questions below.

TABLE 1

Kid	Animal
Nate	elephant
Mario	rabbit
Anita	donkey
Dan	deer
Ada	elephant
Yvette	deer
Leah	elephant
Dom	donkey
Keye	rabbit
Eve	elephant
Tiffany	donkey
Lamar	elephant

TABLE 2

Animal	Number of Votes
elephant	5
rabbit	2
donkey	3
deer	2

1. Which table would you use to find out which animal Anita named? _____
   What animal is it? _____

2. Which table is easier to use to find the animal most kids named? _____
   What animal is it? _____

3. Which table would you use to find out which animal was named by the
   most girls? _____
   How would you do it? _____

4. You want to know how many kids said DONKEY. Which table would tell
   you quickly? _____

5. You want to know *who* said DONKEY. Which table would you use?

   _____

Name _____

CALLING ALL HAMSTERS

The kids in Mr. Cage's class have a new class pet. It's a hamster. They're voting to choose a name for it. The class will use the name that gets the most votes.

The graph shows the results of the class vote. Use it to answer the questions below.

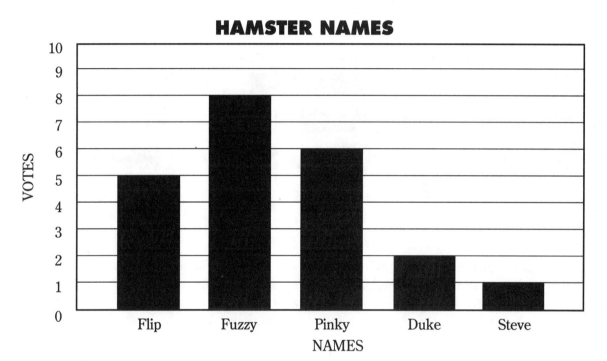

HAMSTER NAMES

1. Why does the graph have five bars? _____
2. Which name got the most votes?_____

   The fewest votes? _____
3. How many students voted?_____

   How do you know? _____
4. How many more students voted for the name Pinky than for Steve? _____
5. What if 3 students who voted for Fuzzy changed their minds and voted for

   Duke instead? What would the hamster's name be?_____
6. Write a paragraph describing what the graph shows. Use the back of

   this paper.

Name _____

GRAPH STUMPERS

1. Only one of the three graphs below shows all the following facts correctly. Circle it.

Kim watched 3 hours of TV.
Lee watched 5 hours of TV.
Ben watched 6 hours of TV.

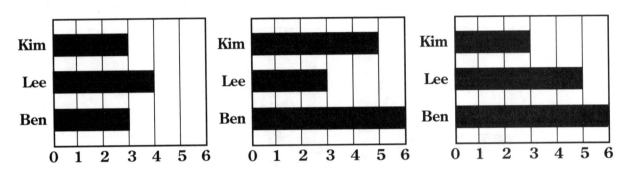

2. Using the graph below, write the name of the appropriate turtle owner on the blank space provided underneath each bar. Use the following facts to help you.

Rick has 4 turtles.
Katy has 7 turtles.
Mei has 6 turtles.

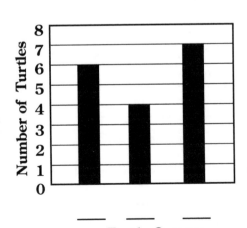

3. Write a paragraph describing the data in the bar graph below.

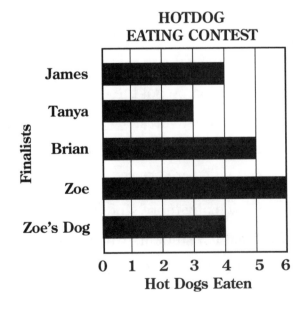

72

A WHALE OF A GRAPH

Many people think that dinosaurs were the biggest animals that ever lived. Some *were* huge. But the largest animal ever may be the blue whale. These ocean giants can weigh as much as 2000 people!

This table gives the length of some whales. Display the same data in a bar graph.

Kind of Whale	Length
blue whale	30 meters
killer whale	8 meters
humpback whale	16 meters
sperm whale	20 meters

To help you plan your graph, answer these questions first.

1. How many bars must your graph have? _____

   Why? _____

2. What else does your graph need? _____

3. Which bar will be the longest? _____

   How do you know? _____

4. Which bar will be twice as long as the killer whale bar? _____

• Use the grid below to make your graph.

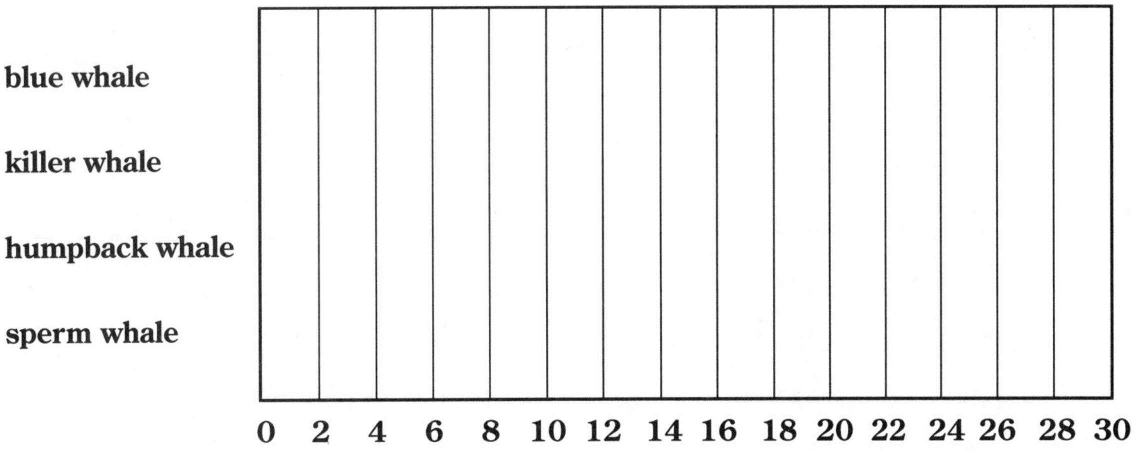

blue whale

killer whale

humpback whale

sperm whale

0 2 4 6 8 10 12 14 16 18 20 22 24 26 28 30

Name _____

WAY TO GO!

How would you most like to travel? Would you like to ride on an elephant's back?
How about flying in a helicopter or a blimp?

Fourth graders at Carr School tallied their choices. The table below shows the results.

	HOW I WOULD MOST LIKE TO TRAVEL
Submarine	~~llll~~ ~~llll~~ ~~llll~~ ~~llll~~ ~~llll~~ llll
Hot-air balloon	~~llll~~ ~~llll~~ ~~llll~~ ~~llll~~ ~~llll~~ ~~llll~~ l
Camel's back	~~llll~~ ~~llll~~
Rocket	~~llll~~ ~~llll~~ ~~llll~~ ~~llll~~ ~~llll~~ ~~llll~~ ~~llll~~ ~~llll~~ ~~llll~~
Dolphin	~~llll~~ ~~llll~~ ~~llll~~ l

Use the data in the tally table to complete the bar graph. The first one has been done for
you. Remember to add title and labels.

Answer these questions about your graph.

1. How did you decide on a title?_____

2. Which way to travel is the favorite? _____

3. What can you say about the travel choice that has the shortest bar?_____

4. Which of the choices would be *your* favorite way to travel?_____

  If you added your vote, how would the results change?_____

Name _____

MEGA-MALL MAKES NEWS

Pretend that you work for a newspaper. Your job is to make graphs.

One day, a reporter hands in a story about a giant new mall in your area. Here's the story that will appear in tomorrow's paper.

The new Milky Way Mega-Mall will be the largest in the state when it opens next week. It will have every kind of store you can think of, and many you would never imagine. For example, there will be 4 button stores, 12 shoelace shops, 9 tomato stores, 14 peanut parlors, and 7 eraser markets. And that's not all! The mall will boast 3 paper clip shops and 1 dog collar boutique. Imagine that!

Make a bar graph below to go with this story. Choose a title. Label the sides. Be sure to include all the data from the newspaper story.

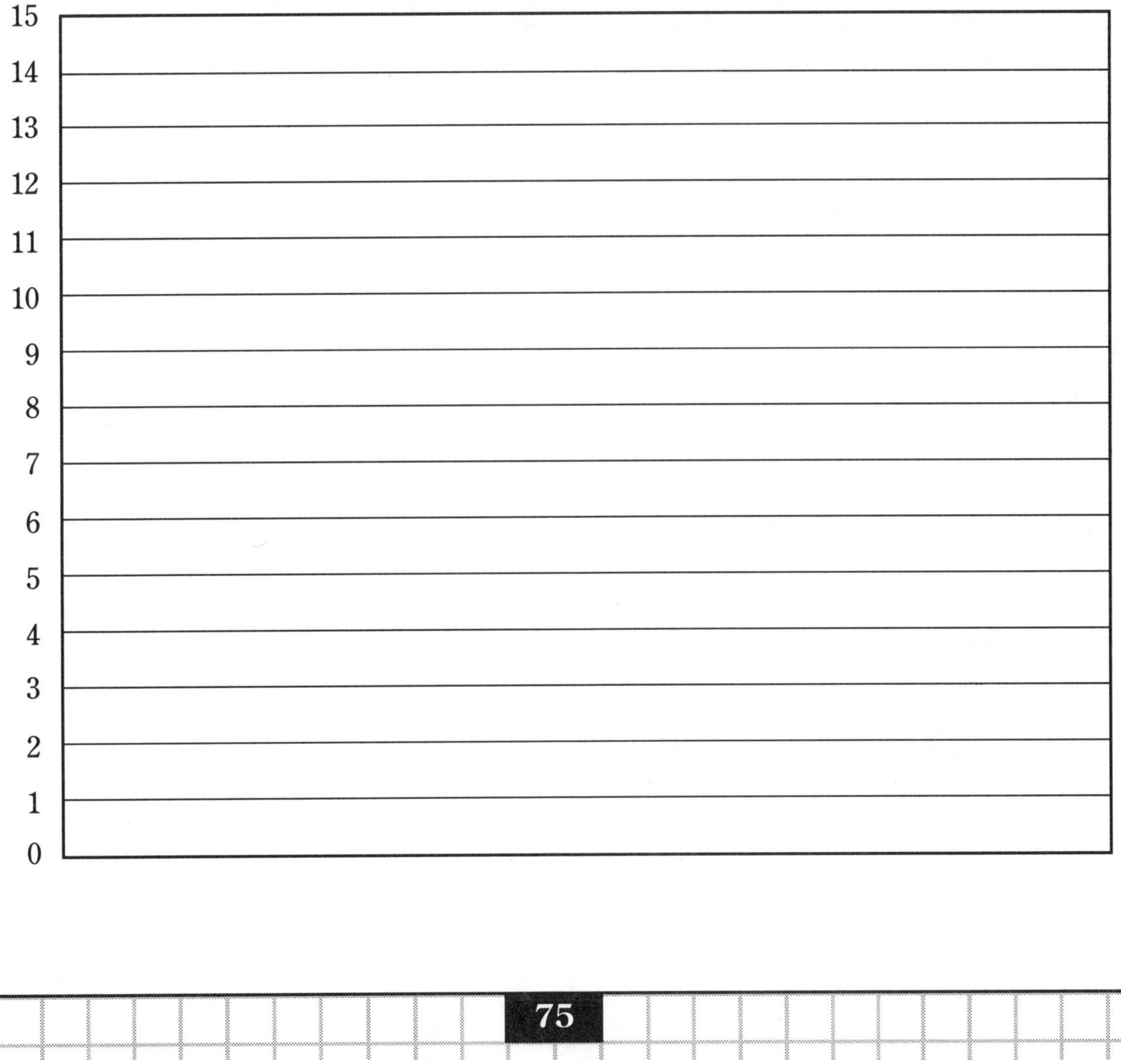

```
15
14
13
12
11
10
 9
 8
 7
 6
 5
 4
 3
 2
 1
 0
```

Name _____

PRIME TIME TALLY

The kids at Dial School and their parents took part in a survey. They were asked to name which night of the week they watch their favorite TV show. They displayed the results in a double bar graph.

Use the information in the graph to answer the questions that follow.

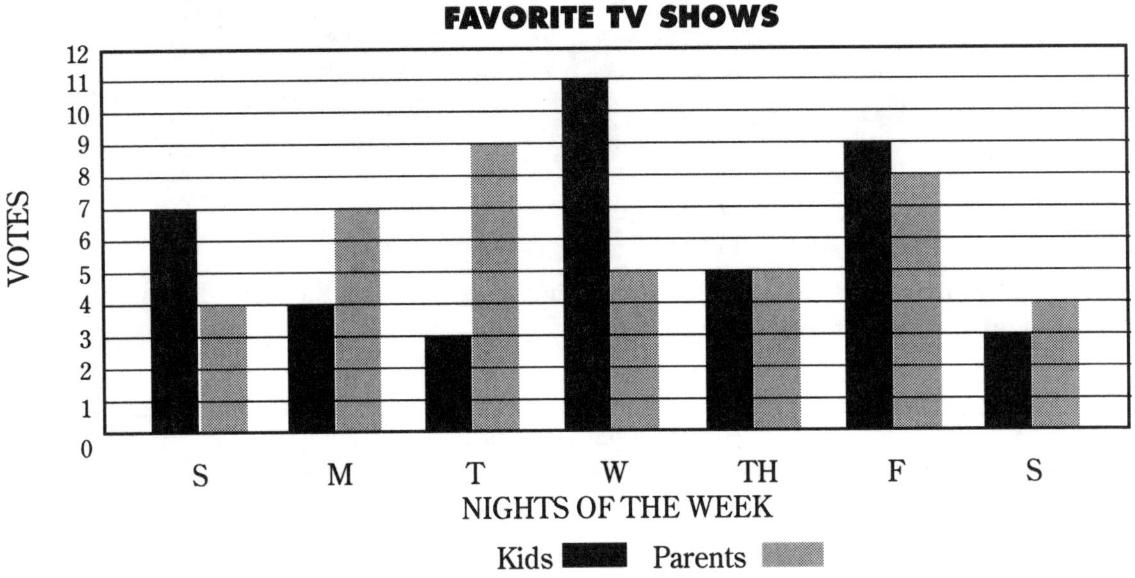

FAVORITE TV SHOWS

VOTES / NIGHTS OF THE WEEK

Kids ■   Parents ▩

1. What information is shown along the vertical side of the graph? _____
   On the horizontal side? _____

2. Why are there two different kinds of bars for each night of the week? _____
   How can you tell what each bar represents? _____

3. Why does the scale go from 0 to 12? _____

4. Which night got the most votes from kids? _____
   From adults? _____

5. Which night did the same number of adults and kids choose as their
   favorite? _____

6. Which night got the greatest number of votes altogether? _____
   How do you know? _____

7. Describe something about TV viewing habits that this graph does not
   show. _____

Name _____

CANS, CANS, AND MORE CANS

It's Earth Day. Some kids are collecting bottles and cans to recycle. They are helping to make the Earth a cleaner place.

The pictograph shows how many cans some kids collected. Use the information to answer the questions that follow.

CANS COLLECTED

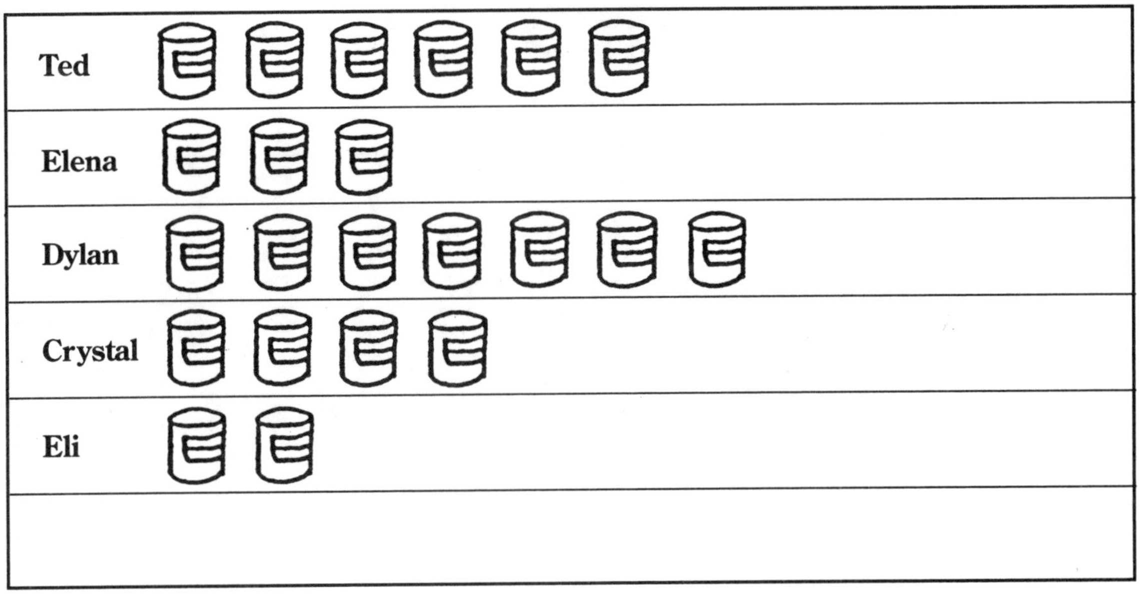

Ted	🥫 🥫 🥫 🥫 🥫 🥫
Elena	🥫 🥫 🥫
Dylan	🥫 🥫 🥫 🥫 🥫 🥫 🥫
Crystal	🥫 🥫 🥫 🥫
Eli	🥫 🥫

🥫 = 5 cans

1. What is the title of the graph? _____

2. How many cans is each 🥫 worth? _____

   How do you know? _____

3. Who collected the most cans? _____

   The fewest cans? _____

4. Who collected 30 cans? _____

5. How many cans did Elena collect? _____

6. How many fewer cans did Eli collect than Crystal? _____

7. Suppose you collected 20 cans on Earth Day. Add this data to the graph.

Name _____

FILL 'EM UP!

It's Food Festival time at Platemore Elementary School. Among other tasty treats, the school is serving burritos. They've ordered 300 chicken burritos, 400 bean burritos, 600 beef burritos, 500 cheese burritos, and 100 chocolate fudge burritos.

Make a pictograph below to compare the burrito orders. Give your graph labels and a title. Draw a picture that stands for 100 burritos. Then answer the questions that follow.

= 100 burritos

1. What if you were to use a symbol that represented 50 burritos? How would this change the way your graph looks? Explain. _____

   _____

2. Would your graph still contain the same data? _____

3. Suppose you were to show the same data using a symbol that stands for 10 burritos. What problems might you have? _____

   _____

Name _____

JUST PASSING THROUGH

Sid's mother collects tolls at the Hannah Clark Bridge. One day Sid went to work with her. While he was there, Sid tallied the different vehicles that passed through her lane. Then he made a pictograph to show the results.

Here's the graph Sid made. But Sid forgot to show what the symbol means!

VEHICLES I COUNTED

Cars	⊕ ⊕ ⊕ ⊕ ⊕ ⊕ ⊕ ⊕ ⊕ ⊕ ⊕
Trucks	⊕ ⊕ ⊕ ⊕ ⊕ ⊕ ⊕ ⊕ ⊕
Motorcycles	⊕ ⊕ ⊕
Buses	⊕ ⊕ ⊕ ⊕ ◖

Sid's mom asked him what each ⊕ stood for. Sid gave her a clue. He said, "May 30th is my birthday. I got excited when the last motorcycle I counted was the 30th one."

1. What does each ⊕ stand for on Sid's graph? _____
   How do you know? _____

2. How many cars passed by? _____
   How many trucks? _____

3. When Sid's brother saw his graph, he laughed. "What does half a tire mean? Did you see half a bus?" Sid explained the meaning of the ◖ to his brother. What do you think he said? _____
   _____

4. How many buses did Sid count? _____

5. After Sid left, an army convoy crossed. It had 25 jeeps. Add this data to the graph.

Name _____

BLOB ON A GRID

Maria brought her blob to school. It's spread out on a coordinate grid on the teacher's desk. That's a picture of it below. All you can see is its outline. It's a see-through blob!

Some points on the grid, like (5,6), lie *inside* the blob. Others, like (1,4), are *outside* the blob. Still others, like (4,8), are right *on* the blob. Use the picture to help you fill in the table.

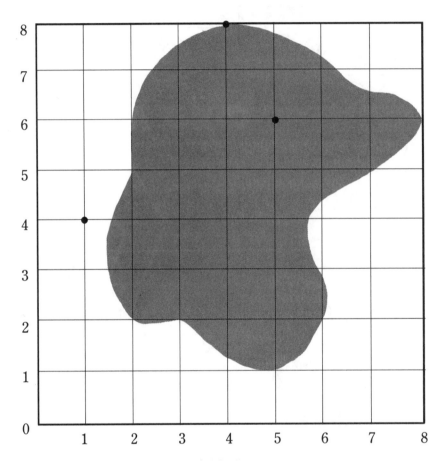

INSIDE, OUTSIDE, or ON THE BLOB

Location	Number Pairs
5 points *inside*	
5 points *outside*	
5 points *on*	

Name _____

I'VE GOT A SECRET

(2,6) (7,7) (1,7) (1,7) (7,4) means "Hello." To see why, just (1,7) (7,4) (7,4) (2,2) at the grid. It has all the alphabet letters. Each letter is on a point you can name by using a number pair.

Use the grid to solve the problems below.

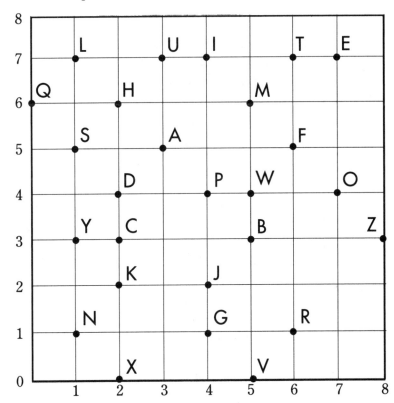

1. This code names a favorite snack. Figure it out.

(4,4) (7,4) (4,4) (2,3) (7,4) (6,1) (1,1)

_____

2. Write your first name in code. _____

3. Here's a riddle. The answer is in code. Can you solve it?

What two words have thousands of letters in them?

(4,4) (7,4) (1,5) (6,7) (7,4) (6,5) (6,5) (4,7) (2,3) (7,7)

_____

4. Write a secret word or message in code. Exchange it with a friend. Solve each other's message. _____

Name _____

TUNA ON RYE WITH TOMATO

Flo's Food Factory is a busy restaurant. It's open from 10:00 A.M. to 9:00 P.M. One day, Flo kept track of the number of customers, hour by hour. She made a line graph to show the changes during the day.

Read Flo's graph. Then answer the questions below.

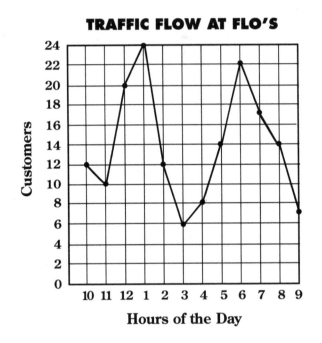

TRAFFIC FLOW AT FLO'S

1. What information is on the left side of the graph? _____

   Along the bottom?_____

2. Describe how the graph looks. _____

3. How can you explain the changes in the graph? _____

   _____

4. When is Flo's the busiest? _____The least busy? _____

5. What if a football team came to Flo's for snacks in the afternoon? How and

   where might the graph change to show this? _____

   _____

Name _____

BELIEVE IT OR NOT

Frank's Famous Frog and Squirrel Show came to town for a week. Folks flocked to see those talented critters perform. They watched them jump, climb, and swim. They heard them sing. They listened to them play the piano. They laughed at their animal jokes. Ha, ha, ha! Everybody had a great time.

The table shows how many people saw the show. Read the table. Then use the data to complete the line graph below.

DAY	S	M	T	W	Th	F	S
PEOPLE	175	75	50	100	75	125	150

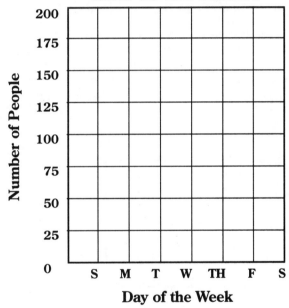

FANS IN THE STANDS

1. Describe what your graph looks like. _____

   _____

2. Why do you think it looks like it does? _____

   _____

3. What if Tuesday had been a school holiday and twice as many fans went

   to the show? How would your graph change? _____

   _____

Name _____

WOOF, WOOF, WOOF

Barkley is Lupe's dog. Every day when Lupe comes home from school, Barkley runs to greet her. He's very excited. He's ready for fun. The happier he is, the more he wags his tail.

Lupe decides to record Barkley's excitement in a line graph. For a week, she keeps track of how many times his tail wags when she comes home. Use the clues that follow to complete the line graph. Be sure to include a title and labels.

1. When Lupe arrived on Monday, she played stick tug-of-war with Barkley. Barkley loved it. He wagged his tail 600 times.

2. On Tuesday, Lupe had a piano lesson. Barkley sulked. He wagged his tail only 100 times.

3. On Wednesday, Lupe brought home the rest of her lunch for Barkley. Barkley was thrilled. He wagged his tail 100 more times than on Monday.

4. On Thursday, Lupe went straight to do her homework. Barkley curled up by her chair. His tail wagged 250 times.

5. On Friday, Lupe stopped at her friend Kat's house first. Kat has cats. Lupe brought home their smell. Barkley went bananas. He wagged his tail 300 more times than on Monday.

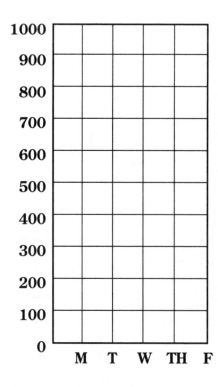

JUST BY THE LOOK OF IT

Look over this page quickly. You'll see three paragraphs and three line graphs. But you *won't* see any numbers.

Each paragraph describes the same information as one of the graphs. Match each paragraph with its graph. Draw a line to connect them.

GRAPH A

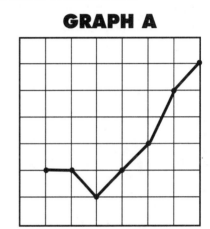

1. Nina's kitchen has a leaky faucet. The leak started slowly—drip...drip...drip. After a few days it got worse. Then it got *much* worse. Finally, Nina called a plumber. The plumber fixed the leak right away.

GRAPH B

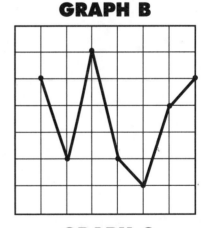

2. Pat's spelling test scores were low. One week they got a little worse. But once she began to study hard, her scores went up.

GRAPH C

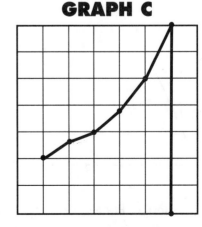

3. Walter has a job feeding pets. He works for people who are very busy. Some go out of town a lot. Walter feeds more pets on weekends than on weekdays. But his busiest day is Tuesday.

DAMP DATA

It rained all day. Rita is trying to read a wet newspaper. She's having a hard time understanding two graphs. Neither graph has labels. No numbers show. Most of each graph has been washed away. Only the lines remain.

The soggy graphs appear below. Look them over. Think about what a graph with that shape might show. Use your imagination. Make up a situation to fit each graph. Write a paragraph about it. Explain why the graph looks the way it does. Write a title for each graph and add labels.

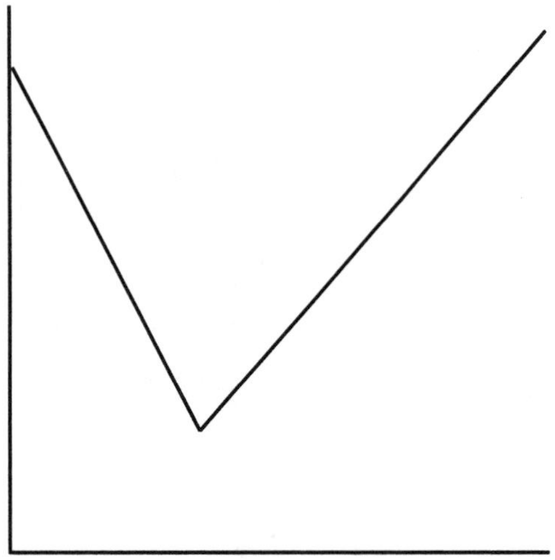

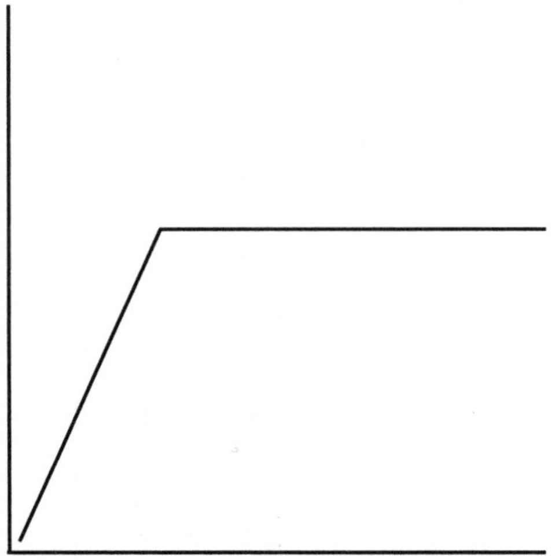

Challenge: Put a scale on each graph. Include actual data in your paragraph.

Mixed-Up Morning, p. 69

FAVORITE RIDES AT THE FAIR

Name of Ride	Number of Votes
Bouncing Bunny Bump	7
Flying Frog	7
Giggle Wheel	3
Zoom-O-Coaster	12

Table Talk, p. 70
1. Table 1; donkey
2. Table 2; elephant
3. Table 1; List girls and their choices.
4. Table 2
5. Table 1

Calling All Hamsters, p. 71
1. 5 name choices
2. Fuzzy; Steve
3. 22; add bar totals
4. 5
5. Pinky
6. Answers will vary.

Graph Stumpers, p. 72
1. Circle third graph on right.
2. Label bars Mei, Rick, Katy.
3. Descriptions will vary.

A Whale Of A Graph, p. 73
1. 4; There are 4 kinds of whales listed in the table.
2. title, labels for axes
3. blue whale; It is the longest of the 4 whales.
4. humpback whale

Titles and labels will vary.

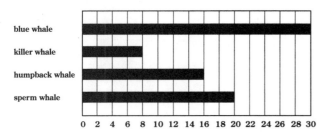

Way To Go!, p. 74
Title and labels will vary.

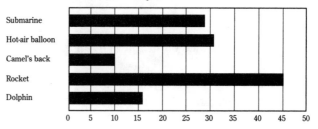

1. It tells what the graph shows.
2. rocket
3. Answers will vary.
4. Answers will vary; Increase by 1.

Mega-Mall Makes News, p. 75
Answers will vary. Check students' work.

Prime Time Tally, p. 76
1. number of votes; days of the week
2. one for kids, one for parents; look at key
3. to include all data
4. Wednesday; Tuesday
5. Thursday
6. Friday; Add double bar totals—17 is greatest total.
7. Answers will vary.

Cans, Cans, And More Cans, p. 77
1. cans collected
2. 5; shown in key
3. Dylan; Eli
4. Ted
5. 15
6. 10
7. Bottom row of graph should show 4 cans.

Fill 'Em Up, p. 78
Titles and labels will vary.

Chicken	🌯🌯🌯
Bean	🌯🌯🌯🌯
Beef	🌯🌯🌯🌯🌯🌯
Cheese	🌯🌯🌯🌯🌯
Chocolate Fudge	🌯

🌯 = 100 burritos

1. Each burrito order would have twice as many symbols, since each symbol is half its original value.
2. yes
3. not enough space on graph to fit all the data

Just Passing Through, p. 79
1. 10 vehicles; 3 tires represent 30 cycles, so 1 tire = 10 vehicles
2. 120; 90
3. half of 10, or 5 vehicles
4. 45
5. Last row of graph should show 2½ tires.

Blob On A Grid, p. 80
Answers will vary.

I've Got A Secret, p. 81
1. POPCORN
2. Answers will vary.
3. POST OFFICE
4. Codes and messages will vary.

Tuna On Rye With Tomato, p. 82
1. number of customers; hours of the day
2. goes sharply up and down twice
3. more customers at lunch and dinner hours; fewer in between
4. 1 p.m.; 3 p.m.
5. Answers will vary but should indicate more customers for an afternoon time or times.

Belive It Or Not, p. 83

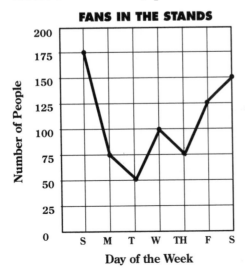

1. rises on the weekend, starting on Friday, drops during the week
2. More people are free to go on the weekend— Friday, Saturday, and Sunday.
3. Graph for Tuesday would show 100 people.

Woof, Woof, Woof, p. 84
Title and labels will vary.

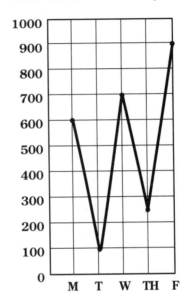

Just By The Look Of It, p. 85
1. Graph C
2. Graph A
3. Graph B

Damp Data, p. 86
Situations, titles, and labels will vary.

Part 3

Reproducible Teacher Resources

Name _____

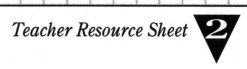

Name _____

	Tallies	Total

Name _____

Teacher Resource Sheet

▲3

92

Name _____

Name _____

5